W9-BXV-831

PRENTICE HALL
LITERATURE

PENGUIN EDITION

Teaching Resources

Unit 4
Poetry

Grade Six

PEARSON

Prentice
Hall

Upper Saddle River, New Jersey
Boston, Massachusetts

This work is protected by United States copyright laws and is provided *solely for the use of teachers and administrators* in teaching courses and assessing student learning in their classes and schools. Dissemination or sale of any part of this work (including on the World Wide Web) will destroy the integrity of the work and is *not* permitted.

Copyright © by Pearson Education, Inc., publishing as Pearson Prentice Hall, Boston, Massachusetts 02116. All rights reserved. Printed in the United States of America. This publication is protected by copyright, and permission should be obtained from the publisher prior to any prohibited reproduction, storage in a retrieval system, or transmission in any form or by any means, electronic, mechanical, photocopying, recording, or likewise. The publisher hereby grants permission to reproduce these pages, in part or in whole, for classroom use only, the number not to exceed the number of students in each class. Notice of copyright must appear on all copies. For information regarding permission(s), write to: Rights and Permissions Department, One Lake Street, Upper Saddle River, New Jersey 07458.

Pearson Prentice Hall™ is a trademark of Pearson Education, Inc.
Pearson® is a registered trademark of Pearson plc.
Prentice Hall® is a registered trademark of Pearson Education, Inc.

ISBN 0-13-165099-8

4 5 6 7 8 9 10   10 09 08 07

Contents

Part 1 Context Clues

The Poetry of Gary Soto

Poetry Collection: Jack Prelutsky, Rosemary and Stephen Vincent Benét, Ogden Nash

Poetry Collection: Maya Angelou, Edgar Allan Poe, Lewis Carroll

Poetry Collection: Eve Merriam, Emily Dickinson, Langston Hughes

Poetry Collection: Sandra Cisneros, Nikki Giovanni, Theodore Roethke

Poetry by Robert Frost and E.E. Cummings

© Pearson Education, Inc., publishing as Pearson Prentice Hall. All rights reserved.

Part 2 Paraphrase

© Pearson Education, Inc., publishing as Pearson Prentice Hall. All rights reserved.

© Pearson Education, Inc., publishing as Pearson Prentice Hall. All rights reserved.

Vocabulary Warm-up Word Lists

Study these words from the poetry of Gary Soto. Then, apply your knowledge to the activities that follow.

Word List A

aisle [EYL] *n.* passage that runs between rows of seats
Stay in your seat, and don't go into the <u>aisle</u> while the plane takes off.

fog [FAHG] *n.* very thick mist
When the rain changed to <u>fog</u>, it became hard to see.

general [JEN er uhl] *n.* a high-ranking military officer
The <u>general</u> is in charge of many soldiers.

pond [PAHND] *n.* very small lake
We can't swim in the <u>pond</u>; the water isn't deep enough.

rooster [ROO ster] *n.* an adult male chicken
The <u>rooster</u> is the big chicken that crows every morning to wake the farm family.

statue [STACH oo] *n.* likeness of a person or animal, often made of stone
There is a famous <u>statue</u> of President Lincoln inside the Lincoln Memorial in Washington, D. C.

Word List B

angles [ANG guhls] *n.* ways of pointing a camera to get a specific shot
If you don't like the picture, move the camera and try some different <u>angles</u>.

fingered [FING erd] *v.* repeatedly touched with fingers
I <u>fingered</u> the gift lightly so I wouldn't break it.

released [ree LEEST] *v.* let go of
When we <u>released</u> the rope, the balloon shot up into the air.

snapshot [SNAP shaht] *n.* a photograph taken in a casual way
Ron used his camera to take a <u>snapshot</u> of his dog.

tiered [TEERD] *adj.* having more than one row or level, like bleacher seats
The movie theater had <u>tiered</u> rows of seats; each one was slightly above the row in front of it.

weighted [WAY ted] *v.* made heavy
The tent was <u>weighted</u> down at the bottom with rocks so it wouldn't blow away.

© Pearson Education, Inc., publishing as Pearson Prentice Hall. All rights reserved.

Name _____ Date _____

The Poetry of Gary Soto
Vocabulary Warm-up Exercises

Exercise A *Fill in each blank in the paragraph below with an appropriate word from Word List A. Use each word only once.*

My sister was marrying an Army [1] _____. She couldn't wait to walk down the [2] _____ at the ceremony. Since I am an artist, I decided to make their wedding gift myself. I built them a [3] _____ to place on the shore of the small [4] _____ on their farm. One day, I walked out to take a look at the place I was going to put it. It was rainy, and the [5] _____ was so thick I could barely see. I almost got lost in the mist. Then I heard the cock-a-doodle-doo of their [6] _____. I followed the sound back to the farmhouse.

Exercise B *Decide whether each statement below is true or false. Circle T or F, then explain your answers.*

1. Something that is <u>weighted</u> down floats easily.
   T / F _____

2. If a driver <u>released</u> his hold on the steering wheel, he might crash.
   T / F _____

3. Photos should be <u>fingered</u> carefully so they don't get dirty.
   T / F _____

4. You can hear voices of people in a <u>snapshot</u>.
   T / F _____

5. Something that is <u>tiered</u> is always flat with a single level.
   T / F _____

6. You can break a camera if you use the wrong <u>angles</u> to take a photo.
   T / F _____

© Pearson Education, Inc., publishing as Pearson Prentice Hall. All rights reserved.

Name _____ Date _____

The Poetry of Gary Soto
Reading Warm-up A

Read the following passage. Pay special attention to the underlined words. Then, read it again, and complete the activities. Use a separate sheet of paper for your written answers.

A. J. had always been shy. In class, he never wanted to raise his hand, even when he knew the answer to a question. When it came to talking to girls—forget about it! His father always told him, "A. J., you should never be afraid. People say silly things. There's nothing wrong with saying something silly yourself, every now and then."

It was easy for his father to be brave. His father was a general in the army. You had to be brave to be a soldier, especially a top-ranking officer like a general.

So when A. J. found himself sitting across the aisle from Amy in the movie theater, it wasn't easy for him to open up his mouth and say "Hi." A. J. had had a crush on Amy for month. Now was his chance to talk to her, if he could gather up the nerve. After the movie, he went up to Amy and asked if he could walk her home. She shocked him by saying yes. Before he knew it, the pair was strolling through George Washington Park.

"It's a spooky evening," she said.

It was. Fog covered the trees, a thick mist that made it hard to see where you were going. It even covered the statue of the famous president at the center of the park. Somehow, he found the words to talk and they chatted all the way to her home. They talked so easily and endlessly that he almost fell into the pond at the edge of the park.

"I don't know how to swim," said Amy. "So be careful, I won't be able to save you."

When they reached Amy's house, she thanked him for walking her home and asked if they could go to the movies together some time.

Afterwards, A. J. was so happy that he almost shouted out loud. If he were a rooster, he would have crowed. If he were a lion, he would have roared.

1. Underline the nearby words that help you know what general means. Then, tell what *general* means.

2. Circle the words that let you know one place an aisle can be found. Then, tell what *aisle* means.

3. Circle the nearby words that have the same meaning as fog. Then, tell what can be hard to do in a *fog*.

4. Circle the words that tell who is the model for the statue. Then, tell what *statue* means.

5. Underline the words that tell what almost happened at the pond. Then, tell how A. J. might have felt if that had happened.

6. Underline the word that tells what kind of sound a rooster makes. Then, tell what *rooster* means.

© Pearson Education, Inc., publishing as Pearson Prentice Hall. All rights reserved.

The Poetry of Gary Soto
Reading Warm-up B

Read the following passage. Pay special attention to the underlined words. Then, read it again, and complete the activities. Use a separate sheet of paper for your written answers.

Ever since photography was invented, one of the most important uses for cameras has been capturing family pictures. There is nothing better than a <u>snapshot</u> for bringing back memories of a special time in family life. Taking photographs is a common activity at major family events like weddings, reunions, and big celebrations. It is a simple activity, too.

For years, photographers used film to take photographs. Recently, however, digital cameras have changed the way people take pictures. These cameras make taking photos easier than before. With film cameras, a person did not know if a shot would come out properly until after the film was processed. With digital cameras, however, a photographer can look at a shot right after the button is <u>released</u>. Using a screen built into the camera, any photograph can be viewed right away. If the photo is not satisfactory, the photographer can try it again, changing <u>angles</u> to improve the picture.

There is another benefit to this as well. Bad photos can be discarded right away. As a result, a photographer does not have to worry about running out of film. In the past many a photographer nervously <u>fingered</u> the camera, knowing they had just a picture or two left. They felt pressure to get the photo right. Now, running out of film is not a problem, since digital cameras do not use film and can store thousands of pictures.

In the old days, photographers were often <u>weighted</u> down with heavy equipment. Now, small light cameras are the rule. Digital cameras can be tiny.

Following a few guidelines can help you to take better pictures. One important rule is simple: Keep short people and small children in front. This <u>tiered</u> arrangement— one row of small people in front of another row of bigger people—will make sure that no one gets left out of the picture.

1. Underline the words that tell what a <u>snapshot</u> can do. Then, tell what a *snapshot* is.

2. Circle the word that tells what is <u>released</u> by a photographer. Then, use the word *released* in a sentence.

3. Circle the words that tell why a photographer might change <u>angles</u>. Then, tell what *angles* means.

4. Underline the word that tells what photographers <u>fingered</u> nervously. Then, tell what *fingered* means.

5. Underline the words that tell what <u>weighted</u> down photographers. Then, describe something that *weighted* you down one time.

6. Underline the type of people who should be in front in this <u>tiered</u> arrangement. Name another place you could find things organized in a *tiered* arrangement.

© Pearson Education, Inc., publishing as Pearson Prentice Hall. All rights reserved.

Gary Soto
Listening and Viewing

Segment 1: Meet Gary Soto
- How did the popular songs of Gary Soto's youth inspire him to write poetry? What music could inspire you to write?

_____

_____

_____

_____

Segment 2: Poetry
- How does Gary Soto "make things new" in his poetry? Why do you think Gary Soto likes to use both made-up and factual details in a poem?

_____

_____

_____

_____

Segment 3: The Writing Process
- Why does Gary Soto use strong images in his poems? According to Gary Soto, no one can write poetry without reading it. Do you agree or disagree with him? Why?

_____

_____

_____

_____

Segment 4: The Rewards of Writing
- How does Gary Soto like to connect with his audience? How do you think literature can bring together all people?

_____

_____

_____

_____

© Pearson Education, Inc., publishing as Pearson Prentice Hall. All rights reserved.

Learning About Poetry

Poetry is different from other types of writing in its appearance, its use of words, and its musical qualities. Two major elements of poetry are **sound devices** and **figurative language.**

Elements of Poetry	Types and Examples
Sound devices can add a musical quality to poetry.	**Rhyme:** the repetition of sounds at the ends of words (*clown, down*) **Rhythm:** the beat created by the pattern of stressed and unstressed syllables (*Ă moŭse lĭvĕs ĭn mў hoŭse.*) **Repetition:** the use of a sound, word, or group of words more than once (*Sunny thoughts filled a sunny day.*) **Onomatopoeia:** the use of words that imitate sounds (*splash, meow*) **Alliteration:** the repetition of consonant sounds at the beginning of words (*a round red rose*)
Figurative language is writing or speech that is not meant to be taken literally. The many types of figurative language are called **figures of speech.**	**Metaphors:** describe one thing as if it were something else (*Courage is a fire that burns in your heart.*) **Similes:** use *like* or *as* to compare two unlike things (*The baby's skin was as soft as silk.*) **Personification:** gives human qualities to a nonhuman thing (*The flowing brook sang a happy song.*)

A. DIRECTIONS: *Each of the following items contains an example of an element of poetry. Underline the correct term.*

rhyme	rhythm	1. Fleet Street
alliteration	onomatopoeia	2. the crunch of snow under our feet
repetition	alliteration	3. a crafty, crawly critter

B. DIRECTIONS: *Follow the directions for each item. Use complete sentences.*

1. Use a simile to write about a big dog.

   _____

2. Use a metaphor to write about happiness.

   _____

3. Use alliteration to write about a snake.

   _____

© Pearson Education, Inc., publishing as Pearson Prentice Hall. All rights reserved.

Name _____ Date _____

The Poetry of Gary Soto
Model Selection: Poetry

"Oranges" and "Ode to Family Photographs" contain **sound devices** and **figurative language.** This chart reviews these two major elements of poetry.

Elements of Poetry	Types and Examples
Sound devices can add a musical quality to poetry.	**Rhyme:** the repetition of sounds at the ends of words (*clown, down*) **Rhythm:** the beat created by the pattern of stressed and unstressed syllables (*Ă moúse livĕs ín mў hoúse.*) **Repetition:** the use of a sound, word, or group of words more than once (*Sunny thoughts filled a sunny day.*) **Onomatopoeia:** the use of words that imitate sounds (*splash, meow*) **Alliteration:** the repetition of consonant sounds at the beginning of words (*a round red rose*)
Figurative language is writing or speech that is not meant to be taken literally. The many types of figurative language are called **figures of speech.**	**Metaphors:** describe one thing as if it were something else (*Courage is a fire that burns in your heart.*) **Similes:** use *like* or *as* to compare two unlike things (*The baby's skin was as soft as silk.*) **Personification:** gives human qualities to a nonhuman thing (*The flowing brook sang a happy song.*)

DIRECTIONS: *Answer these questions about the elements in Gary Soto's poems.*

1. What figure of speech is used in "I turned to the candies/Tiered like bleachers"?

_____

2. In "Oranges," a tiny bell brings the saleslady. Give two examples of onomatopoeia that could be used to describe the sound of the bell.

_____

3. "The saleslady's eyes met mine,/And held them, knowing/Very well what it was all/About." What figure of speech is used in these lines?

_____

4. Use stress marks to mark the rhythm in the line "This is the pond, and these are my feet."

_____

© Pearson Education, Inc., publishing as Pearson Prentice Hall. All rights reserved.

Name _____ Date _____

The Poetry of Gary Soto
Selection Test A

Learning About Poetry *Identify the letter of the choice that best answers the question.*

____ 1. Which of the following contains an example of rhyme?
   A. Let us go / through the snow.
   B. Stop, stop / that staggering steer!
   C. On your mark, / get ready, / let's go!
   D. The siren wailed, / shattering the silence of the night.

____ 2. Which of the following contains an example of onomatopoeia?
   A. The horse ran around the ring.
   B. The clock ticked loudly.
   C. The room looked messy.
   D. The sand felt rough.

____ 3. Which of the following contains an example of repetition?
   A. The stars lit up the sky last night.
   B. Starlight stayed with us until dawn.
   C. Twinkle, twinkle, little star.
   D. Are there stars near Mars?

____ 4. What figure of speech is used in *She's as busy as a bee?*
   A. simile
   B. metaphor
   C. personification
   D. alliteration

____ 5. What figure of speech is used in *The cool forest welcomed the hot and tired campers?*
   A. metaphor
   B. personification
   C. simile
   D. onomatopoeia

© Pearson Education, Inc., publishing as Pearson Prentice Hall. All rights reserved.

Critical Reading

____ 6. What element of poetry appears in these lines from "Oranges"?
   Outside,/A few cars hissing past
   A. metaphor
   B. onomatopoeia
   C. simile
   D. personification

____ 7. Which of the following BEST describes the setting of "Oranges"?
   A. summer, in a park
   B. fall, by the ocean
   C. winter, in a city
   D. spring, in a store

____ 8. In "Oranges," why does the speaker put one orange on the counter of the drug store?
   A. He wants to use it to pay for half of the candy the girl chooses.
   B. He wants to give it to the girl he brought to the drug store.
   C. He wants to throw it away because it isn't ripe.
   D. He wants the saleslady to give it to the girl he brought to the drug store.

____ 9. Which of the following is the BEST summary of "Oranges"?
   A. A boy compares a bright orange to a bright fire.
   B. A boy describes the experiences he had during his first walk with a girl.
   C. A boy meets a kind woman at a drug store.
   D. A boy and a girl stop for chocolate candy at a drug store.

____ 10. In "Ode to Family Photographs," the speaker says "Mamá was never good at pictures." What does he mean?
   A. Mamá was not very good at taking photographs.
   B. Mamá was not very good at drawing pictures.
   C. Mamá did not like to appear in photographs.
   D. Mamá did not enjoy taking photographs.

____ 11. According to the speaker in "Ode to Family Photographs," what proves that everyone had fun when Mamá took pictures?
   A. They are all at the zoo.
   B. They are all eating chocolate.
   C. They are all laughing.
   D. They are all singing.

© Pearson Education, Inc., publishing as Pearson Prentice Hall. All rights reserved.

___ 12. What figure of speech appears in this line from "Ode to Family Photographs"?
The angles dizzy as a spin on a merry-go-round.

A. onomatopoeia

B. alliteration

C. metaphor

D. simile

___ 13. Which statement is true about both "Oranges" and "Ode to Family Photographs"?

A. Each poem is about a family trip.

B. Each poem is about people laughing and having fun.

C. Both poems are about happy memories.

D. Both poems take place on a cold, gray day.

___ 14. An ode is a song or poem that shows respect and deep feelings. Think about "Ode to Family Photographs." Which statement tells why the speaker has such deep feelings about the family photographs?

A. His mother was a great photographer.

B. He misses his brother Pedro.

C. He has fond memories of eating candy.

D. He has fond memories of family fun.

Essay

15. Gary Soto often uses a character's words or actions to give clues about what type of person that character is. What type of person do you think the saleslady at the drug store in "Oranges" is? Support your answer with details from the poem.

16. Which poem did you like better, "Oranges" or "Ode to Family Photographs"? Explain why, using details from the poem.

© Pearson Education, Inc., publishing as Pearson Prentice Hall. All rights reserved.

Name _____ Date _____

The Poetry of Gary Soto
Selection Test B

Learning About Poetry *Identify the letter of the choice that best completes the statement or answers the question.*

____ 1. The repetition of sounds within a line or at the ends of lines is called
   A. rhythm.
   B. alliteration.
   C. rhyme.
   D. onomatopoeia.

____ 2. The line *The clock told me it was time to leave* contains an example of
   A. metaphor.
   B. personification.
   C. simile.
   D. onomatopoeia.

____ 3. The line *The best of days with the best of friends* contains an example of
   A. metaphor.
   B. rhyme.
   C. onomatopoeia.
   D. repetition.

____ 4. Lines of poetry contain stressed syllables and unstressed syllables. This element of poetry is called
   A. rhythm.
   B. alliteration.
   C. rhyme.
   D. repetition.

____ 5. What element of poetry appears in the line *Her skin was as white as snow?*
   A. metaphor
   B. personification
   C. simile
   D. onomatopoeia

____ 6. Which of the following items most likely got its name due to onomatopoeia?
   A. basketball
   B. groundhog
   C. doorbell
   D. popcorn

Critical Reading

____ 7. What element of poetry appears in this line from "Ode to Family Photographs"?
   The angles dizzy as a spin on a merry-go-round.

   A. metaphor
   B. onomatopoeia
   C. simile
   D. repetition

© Pearson Education, Inc., publishing as Pearson Prentice Hall. All rights reserved.

____ 8. What element of poetry appears in this line from "Oranges"?
      A dog barked at me, until/She came out pulling/At her gloves
    A. alliteration
    B. onomatopoeia
    C. simile
    D. rhyme

____ 9. Gary Soto compares the bright color of an orange with the color of a fire. Which of the following lines expresses that thought as a metaphor?
    A. The orange was as bright as a fire.
    B. The orange was like a fire in his hands.
    C. The orange peel crackled like a fire.
    D. The orange was a fire in his hands.

____ 10. Which statement is the best summary of "Oranges"?
    A. The speaker remembers photographs that his mother took of the family.
    B. The speaker remembers going to a drug store to buy candy.
    C. The speaker remembers the first time he went for a walk with a girl.
    D. The speaker remembers a cold day in December.

____ 11. In "Oranges," what problem must the speaker solve?
    A. The girl's dog barks and barks at him.
    B. He doesn't have enough money to pay for the chocolate.
    C. He's not sure how to get home from the drug store.
    D. It is a very cold day, and he has trouble staying warm.

____ 12. Which of the following of Gary Soto's lines uses simile?
    A. "I was making a fire in my hands."
    B. "Fog hanging like old/Coats between the trees."
    C. "That was so bright against/The gray of December"
    D. "Bringing a saleslady/Down a narrow aisle of goods."

____ 13. Which is the best paraphrase of the line "Mamá was never good at pictures"?
    A. Mamá didn't like to go to the movies.
    B. Mamá wasn't very good at drawing pictures.
    C. Mamá wasn't very good at taking photographs.
    D. Mamá wasn't very good at hanging pictures on a wall.

____ 14. In "Ode to Family Photographs," what does the speaker mean when he says, "And this is me with my head cut off"?
    A. The photograph shows only his body, and his head is out of the picture.
    B. Someone has cut the photograph so that his head is now missing.
    C. He was playing a game and pretending that he didn't have a head.
    D. He was hiding behind a tree, so his head was not in the picture.

© Pearson Education, Inc., publishing as Pearson Prentice Hall. All rights reserved.

____ 15. According to the speaker in "Ode to Family Photographs," why are many of the photographs blurry?
A. The people were moving too quickly.
B. It was a windy day.
C. His mother sneezed while using the camera.
D. The camera was broken.

____ 16. According to the speaker in "Ode to Family Photographs," what is true of all the pictures?
A. They are in an album.
B. They show people laughing and having fun.
C. They show people at a zoo.
D. They show people standing on a rock.

____ 17. Which word from "Ode to Family Photographs" is an example of onomatopoeia?
A. pretzel
B. smear
C. snapshot
D. merry-go-round

____ 18. Which statement is true about both "Oranges" and "Ode to Family Photographs"?
A. Both poems are about Soto's family.
B. Both poems are about solving problems.
C. Both poems are about happy memories.
D. Both poems are about learning how to do something.

Essay

19. Imagine that you are the saleslady in the poem "Oranges." Write a summary of the events that took place that day in your drug store and describe how they made you feel.

20. In your opinion, why are the photographs in "Ode to Family Photographs" important to the speaker? Use details from the poem to support your view.

21. Which of the poems, "Oranges" or "Ode to Family Photographs," do you feel more closely connected to? Use details from the poem to explain why.

© Pearson Education, Inc., publishing as Pearson Prentice Hall. All rights reserved.

Unit 4: Poetry
Part 1 Concept Map

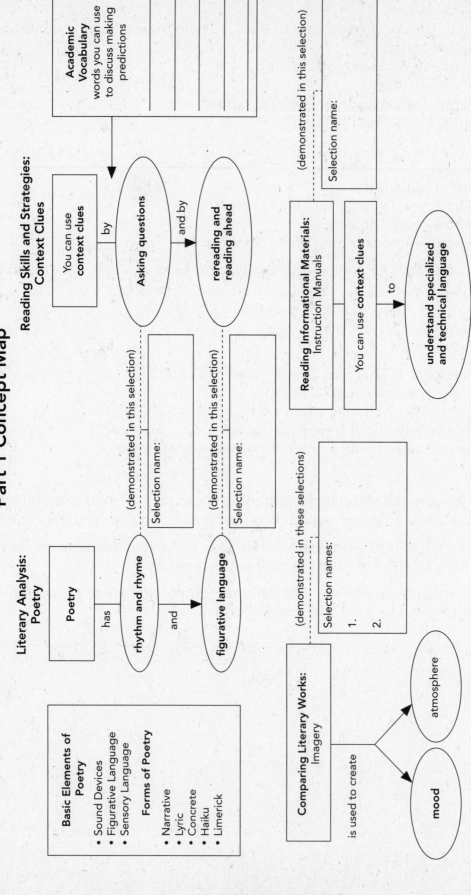

Reading Skills and Strategies: Context Clues

You can use context clues → by → Asking questions → and by → rereading and reading ahead

(demonstrated in this selection)

Selection name: _____

(demonstrated in this selection)

Selection name: _____

Academic Vocabulary words you can use to discuss making predictions

Literary Analysis: Poetry

Poetry → has → rhythm and rhyme → and → figurative language

Basic Elements of Poetry
• Sound Devices
• Figurative Language
• Sensory Language

Forms of Poetry
• Narrative
• Lyric
• Concrete
• Haiku
• Limerick

Comparing Literary Works: Imagery

Imagery → is used to create → atmosphere / mood

(demonstrated in these selections)

Selection names:
1.
2.

Reading Informational Materials: Instruction Manuals

You can use context clues → to → understand specialized and technical language

(demonstrated in this selection)

Selection name: _____

Part 1 Student Log

Complete this chart to track your assignments.

Writing	Extend Your Learning	Writing Workshop	Other Assignments

© Pearson Education, Inc., publishing as Pearson Prentice Hall. All rights reserved.

Unit 4: Poetry
Part 1 Diagnostic Test 7

MULTIPLE CHOICE

Read the selection. Then, answer the questions that follow.

For thousands of years, humans had tried to fly. And although every attempt failed, that did not stop people from trying. Watching birds fly made humans long for the freedom of flight. Then, during the 15th Century, Leonardo da Vinci turned to the study of flight. Like many before him, Leonardo based his ideas on the wings of birds. He made drawings of flying machines with bird-like flapping wings. However, none of them ever got off the ground.

Then, 500 years later, Leonardo's theory finally took flight. On December 2, 2003, Angelo D'Arrigo flew a model of Leonardo's flying machine, the *Piuma*, meaning feather. The event took place in the Italian town where Leonardo was born.

D'Arrigo and his team followed Leonardo's drawings in all ways, using modern materials, such as aluminum tubes and a synthetic fiber. These materials made the model about 170 pounds lighter than Leonardo's original machine.

The *Piuma* was tested in a wind tunnel. When the wind reached nearly 22 miles per hour, the machine took off, carrying D'Arrigo. The test flight lasted for two hours.

Leonardo dared to think beyond the limits of his age. Now, at last, one of his most daring ideas has been set free.

1. What inspired people to want to fly?
   A. They needed a faster way of transportation.
   B. They wanted to be able to cross the oceans quickly.
   C. They wanted to be able to see the world from up high.
   D. They wanted the freedom that the birds had.

2. When was the first true flying machine designed?
   A. in ancient times
   B. in the fifteenth century
   C. in the twentieth century
   D. in 1452

3. On what did Leonardo model his flying machine?
   A. on a falling leaf
   B. on a floating feather
   C. on the wings of a bird
   D. on wind

4. Which detail leads you to conclude that the materials Leonardo used in his model were too heavy to fly?
   A. D'Arrigo's model was 170 pounds lighter than Leonardo's machine.
   B. Leonardo's model was of a machine with birdlike flapping wings.
   C. Leonardo based his ideas on the wings of birds.
   D. Angelo D'Arrigo flew a model of Leonardo's flying machine.

5. How was D'Arrigo's model different from Leonardo's model?
   A. He used a totally different design.
   B. His model had a powerful engine.
   C. His model was named the *Piuma*.
   D. He used modern lightweight materials.

© Pearson Education, Inc., publishing as Pearson Prentice Hall. All rights reserved.

6. How was D'Arrigo's model the same as Leonardo's model?
   A. He used the same type of materials that Leonardo used.
   B. He used Leonardo's model drawing in all its details.
   C. He used the same type of engine that Leonardo used.
   D. His model was based on the shape of a feather, just like Leonardo's model.

7. How did D'Arrigo test the model?
   A. He tested it at a local airport.
   B. He flew it from the top of a high hill.
   C. He used a wind tunnel.
   D. He tested it during a high wind.

8. What did D'Arrigo prove by flying the *Piuma*?
   A. that it is possible for people to build a new style of airplane
   B. that Leonardo's design was workable
   C. that he is a better builder than Leonardo
   D. that many types of planes are possible

Read the selection. Then, answer the questions that follow.

The early blacksmith was a muscular man covered in soot. He toiled all day making and repairing metal objects such as pots and pans, farm implements and tools, fences, horseshoes, and nails.

The one-room blacksmith's shop was kept dark so he could judge the temperature of the metal he heated in the forge. In the center of the room stood a large metal anvil on which the blacksmith pounded the hot iron into shape with an enormous hammer. Next to the anvil stood a bucket of water. Near that was a collection of tools.

The blacksmith heated iron in the flaming forge until it turned soft. Then he dipped it into the bucket of water to cool it before pounding the metal into its desired form. When the iron became too cool, he returned it to the forge to re-heat. He had to keep the temperature within a certain range. If the iron grew too hot it became too soft to shape. If it grew too cold it would break.

From colonial days until the early 1900s, the clang of the blacksmith's hammer was a familiar sound in most towns and villages. Today the village blacksmith is no longer a central figure in our society, but he still earns our respect.

9. What kind of work did a blacksmith do?
   A. toiled building fences for horses
   B. kept a shop
   C. labored removing soot
   D. repaired metal objects

10. Which detail explains why blacksmiths were so muscular?
    A. They toiled all day.
    B. They used enormous hammers.
    C. They used a variety of tools.
    D. They made metal objects.

11. Why would a blacksmith keep his shop dark?
    A. because the fire from the forge provided all the light that was necessary
    B. so he could see when the metal he was working on turned red hot
    C. because the fire on the forge was so hot additional light would add to the heat
    D. because he worked mainly during the day and did not need additional light

12. On what object did the blacksmith pound the metal on which he was working?

    A. the anvil   **C.** the hammer

    B. the forge   **D.** the bucket of water

13. Why did the blacksmith need both the forge and water to shape metal?

    A. to heat the metal and then to reshape it in the water   **C.** to clean and cool down the metal before heating it in the forge

    B. to heat the metal and to wash off dust and dirt from the metal   **D.** to keep the metal exactly the right temperature to work

14. What happened to the metal on which a blacksmith worked if it grew too hot?

    A. It would become too hard to shape.   **C.** It would become too soft to shape.

    B. It would turn into a liquid.   **D.** It would splinter into small pieces.

15. Which detail might explain why the blacksmith still earns respect today?

    A. He toiled all day at a difficult job.   **C.** He was muscular.

    B. He had a collection of tools.   **D.** He worked in a one-room shop.

© Pearson Education, Inc., publishing as Pearson Prentice Hall. All rights reserved.

Vocabulary Warm-up Word Lists

Study these words from the poems. Then apply your knowledge to the activities that follow.

Word List A

bulged [BULJD] *v.* swelled or stuck out
My backpack <u>bulged</u> from all the books I jammed into it.

confident [KAHN fuh duhnt] *adj.* sure in your self, sure about something
Kit had climbed the mountain before, so he was <u>confident</u> he could do it again.

cross [KRAWS] *adj.* mad, unhappy
What are you mad about? You have such a <u>cross</u> look on your face.

daring [DAIR ing] *adj.* brave
I'm not <u>daring</u> enough to swim in those rough waves.

discouraged [dis KER ijd] *adj.* feeling like you have lost your confidence or enthusiasm
When the other team took the lead, our players became <u>discouraged</u>.

praised [PRAYZD] *v.* gave compliments, said words of approval
My teacher <u>praised</u> me for writing such a good paper.

Word List B

devoted [di VOH tid] *adj.* loyal to a person, thing, or idea
I could never let her down; I'm too <u>devoted</u> to her.

fortress [FAWR tris] *v.* a large strong building that is used to keep safe from attacks
Inside the <u>fortress</u>, the soldiers were safe from enemy bombs.

glider [GLY duhr] *n.* small light plane that flies without the power of an engine
A <u>glider</u> is very quiet in the air because there is no engine noise.

minuscule [MIN i skyool] *adj.* tiny
The bug was <u>minuscule</u>, smaller than an ant.

murmur [MER muhr] *v.* talk very softly
When you <u>murmur</u> like that, I can barely hear you.

satchel [SACH uhl] *n.* small bag or suitcase
The construction worker carried all his tools in his <u>satchel</u>.

© Pearson Education, Inc., publishing as Pearson Prentice Hall. All rights reserved.

Poetry Collection by Ogden Nash, Jack Prelutsky, and Rosemary and Stephen Vincent Benét
Vocabulary Warm-up Exercises

Exercise A *Fill in each blank in the paragraph below with an appropriate word from Word List A. Use each word only once.*

Samantha felt [1] _____ when her brother said she shouldn't try out for the soccer team. Still, she decided not to be [2] _____ by his mean words. She was [3] _____ in her abilities; she had been playing for years.

The tryouts were tough. A bruise [4] _____ out on her leg where someone had kicked her. Sam didn't notice the pain. She was too happy. When the coach [5] _____ her skills, she knew she had made the team.

"You're a very [6] _____ player," he said. "You're not afraid of anything!"

Exercise B *Answer the questions with complete explanations.*

1. Can a car fit into a <u>satchel</u>?
   _____

2. Would a person be <u>devoted</u> to someone who is their enemy?
   _____

3. Is it easy to knock down a <u>fortress</u>?
   _____

4. Can the engine fail on a <u>glider</u>?
   _____

5. What would you consider a <u>minuscule</u> dinner?
   _____

6. Describe a situation in which you might want to <u>murmur</u>.
   _____

© Pearson Education, Inc., publishing as Pearson Prentice Hall. All rights reserved.

Poetry Collection by Ogden Nash, Jack Prelutsky, and Rosemary and Stephen Vincent Benét
Reading Warm-up A

Read the following passage. Pay special attention to the underlined words. Then, read it again, and complete the activities. Use a separate sheet of paper for your written answers.

King Kong and Godzilla are scary creatures that don't exist in real life. They aren't the only ones, however. Another creature that has inspired fear, but has never really existed, is the Loch Ness monster. Fans of the monster call the beast "Nessie."

Loch Ness is a big lake in Scotland. For over a thousand years, people have told stories about a giant monster that lived in the lake. The stories were frightening to children. Some thought it was a <u>daring</u> act to even go near the lake. Who could be so brave?

Carvings showing the monster were found on ancient stones. These pictures showed a strange animal with a forehead that <u>bulged</u> out, a long strange beak, and flippers instead of feet. It looked a bit like a swimming elephant. Over the years, many people claimed to have seen something similar in Loch Ness. They described it in many different ways. Some people even took pictures. No one could prove that pictures showed a real monster.

Many scientists, however, were <u>confident</u> that no monster would be found in the lake. They were sure that it wasn't possible for such a creature to exist. In 2003, a search team went to Loch Ness. They used special equipment to search the bottom of the lake. No giant monster was found.

The team members were <u>praised</u> by other scientists for putting an end to a story that wasn't true. Not everyone, however, was happy about the outcome. Some "Nessie" fans were <u>cross</u> when they heard the news. They were mad because they wanted to believe that "Nessie" really existed. Others, however, weren't <u>discouraged</u> by the findings. They still think that the monster is hiding in the lake. Somehow, they believe, scientists simply missed the place where it was hiding.

1. Underline the nearby word that has the same meaning as <u>daring</u>. Then, describe something you think is *daring*.

2. Circle the words that tell you what <u>bulged</u> out. Then, tell what *bulged* means.

3. Circle the nearby word that has a similar meaning to <u>confident</u>. Then, tell about what the scientists were *confident*.

4. Circle the words that tell why the team members were <u>praised</u>. Then, tell what *praised* means.

5. Underline the nearby word that has a similar meaning to <u>cross</u>. Then, describe something that would make you feel *cross*.

6. Underline the words that tell why others weren't <u>discouraged</u>. Then, tell what *discouraged* means.

© Pearson Education, Inc., publishing as Pearson Prentice Hall. All rights reserved.

Poetry Collection by Ogden Nash, Jack Prelutsky, and Rosemary and Stephen Vincent Benét
Reading Warm-up B

Read the following passage. Pay special attention to the underlined words. Then, read it again, and complete the activities. Use a separate sheet of paper for your written answers.

The Wright brothers worked long and hard to prove that human flight was possible. At first, they built a glider to take to the air, a small plane without an engine. The glider was quiet; you could hear yourself murmur while flying since there was no engine.

In December 1903, the Wright brothers made history with an engine-powered plane. It wasn't much by today's standards. In the century since their achievement, airplane engineers have been devoted to one task—building better planes.

Better often meant bigger since the first planes were small. They didn't have overhead bins for storing luggage, and they didn't have huge cargo areas in the bottom of the plane. Inside the cockpits, there was barely room for a pilot and a satchel. Over time, engineers developed much larger and roomier planes.

Many big planes were invented for the military. The Armed Forces needed big planes for holding weapons and carrying troops and equipment. One example is the B-17. The B-17 was used by the United States during World War II. It was often called the flying fortress. Like a heavily protected building, the plane could defend itself. It had thirteen machine guns placed in different spots on the plane.

Other big planes were developed for passenger travel. By the 1940s and 1950s, air travel was becoming more popular than travel by train. Big planes were needed to carry people from one city to another. In 1970, the first "Jumbo Jet" was introduced: the Boeing 747. This plane had a very wide body and could carry 400 passengers.

Today, companies are still working on bigger and better planes. The new Airbus A380 makes other planes look minuscule by comparison. The A380 is a huge plane that will hold between five hundred and a thousand passengers.

1. Underline the words that tell what a glider does not have. Then, tell what a *glider* is.

2. Circle the words that explain why you could hear yourself murmur. Then, use the word *murmur* in a sentence.

3. Circle the words that tell what engineers were devoted to doing. Then, tell what *devoted* means.

4. Underline the words that explain why there was barely room for a satchel in the first planes. Then, tell what a *satchel* is.

5. Underline the words that explain what kind of building a fortress is. Then, use the word *fortress* in a sentence.

6. Underline the words that tell what looks minuscule compared to the A380. Then, list three other words with a similar meaning to *minuscule*.

© Pearson Education, Inc., publishing as Pearson Prentice Hall. All rights reserved.

Name _____ Date _____

Reading: Ask Questions to Use Context Clues

When you come across a word you do not know or a word used in an unusual way, you can sometimes figure out the meaning by using context clues. **Context clues** are found in the words, phrases, and sentences surrounding an unfamiliar word. They may be words that have the same meaning or that describe or explain the word. To use context clues, **ask questions** such as these:

- *What kind of word is it?*
- *What word can I use in place of it?*
- *Which other words in the sentence explain it?*

DIRECTIONS: *Use this chart to figure out the meaning of some words that you may not know or that are used in an unusual way in the poems in this collection. For each item, write the question you would ask to figure out the meaning of the underlined word or words. Then, answer the question. Finally, write the meaning of the word or expression. The first item has been done for you.*

Word in Context	Question	Answer	Meaning
1. there wasn't a thing on its <u>minuscule</u> mind	Which words explain what the unfamiliar word means?	"there wasn't a thing on its . . . mind"	little
2. its tail was a <u>cudgel</u> of gristle and bone			
3. "These birds are very <u>trying</u>. / I'm sick of hearing them . . ."			
4. They sometimes skinned their noses. / For learning how to rule the air / Was <u>not a bed of roses</u>—			
5. The witch's face was <u>cross</u> and wrinkled			

© Pearson Education, Inc., publishing as Pearson Prentice Hall. All rights reserved.

Name _____ Date _____

Poetry Collection: Jack Prelutsky, Rosemary and Stephen Vincent Benét, Ogden Nash
Literary Analysis: Rhythm and Rhyme

Poets often use **rhythm** and **rhyme** to add a musical quality to their poems. **Rhythm** is the sound pattern created by stressed and unstressed syllables. Stressed syllables receive more emphasis than unstressed syllables. In this example, capital letters indicate the stressed syllables:

CLANK-i-ty CLANK-i-ty CLANK-i-ty CLANK! (4 stressed syllables, 6 unstressed syllables)

AN-ky-lo-SAUR-us was BUILT like a TANK (4 stressed syllables, 6 unstressed syllables)

Rhyme is the repetition of sounds at the ends of words, such as *clank* and *tank*. Once a rhyme pattern, or rhyme scheme, has been established, you come to expect the upcoming rhymes. Many traditional poems have rhyming words at the ends of lines.

DIRECTIONS: *Rewrite each of the following lines from the poems to show their rhythm and rhyme. Write each syllable separately, as in the example above. Use capital letters to show stressed syllables. Then, circle the words that rhyme.*

1. Ankylosaurus was best left alone / Its tail was a cudgel of gristle and bone

   _____

   _____

2. They glided here, they glided there, / They sometimes skinned their noses./—For learning how to rule the air / Was not a bed of roses—

   _____

   _____

   _____

   _____

3. The giant was hairy, the giant was horrid, / He had one eye in the middle of his forehead. Good morning Isabel, the giant said, / I'll grind your bones to make my bread.

   _____

   _____

   _____

   _____

© Pearson Education, Inc., publishing as Pearson Prentice Hall. All rights reserved.

Name _____ Date _____

Vocabulary Builder

Word List

inedible	ravenous	rancor

A. DIRECTIONS: *Write the word from the Word List that best completes each sentence.*

1. After their long hike, the campers were _____ for dinner.
2. The tough meat we were served in the cafeteria was _____.
3. Surprisingly, the woman who had been wrongfully held in jail showed no _____.

B. DIRECTIONS: *Answer each question using a complete sentence. In your answer, use a word from the Word List in place of the underlined words.*

1. When would someone be <u>greedily hungry</u>?

_____

_____

2. What terrible thing might cause someone to feel <u>bitter hate</u>?

_____

_____

3. What kind of food would be considered <u>not fit to be eaten</u>?

_____

_____

C. DIRECTIONS: *On each line, write the letter of the word that means* the same as *the word from the Word List.*

____ 1. inedible
    A. tasty   **B.** indigestible   **C.** delicious   **D.** nutritious

____ 2. ravenous
    A. full   **B.** empty   **C.** loud   **D.** hungry

____ 3. rancor
    A. pity   **B.** friendship   **C.** hatred   **D.** love

© Pearson Education, Inc., publishing as Pearson Prentice Hall. All rights reserved.

Poetry Collection: Jack Prelutsky, Rosemary and Stephen Vincent Benét, Ogden Nash
Support for Writing a Letter to an Author

Use this form to draft a **letter to the author** of "Ankylosaurus," "Wilbur Wright and Orville Wright," or "Adventures of Isabel." Be sure to state your reaction to the poem and tell whether or not you like the poem. Include reasons for your reaction, and refer to the poem to support your reasons.

Heading: Your address and the date _____

_____

_____

Inside Address: Where the letter will be sent _____

_____

_____

Greeting

Begin **body** of letter. *State your over-all reaction.*

Dear _____,

_____

_____

_____

State reasons for your reaction, and give examples to support reasons.

_____

_____

_____

_____

_____

_____

_____

Closing and **Signature** _____

_____

Now, write a final draft of your letter to the author of one of the poems in this collection.

© Pearson Education, Inc., publishing as Pearson Prentice Hall. All rights reserved.

Name _____ Date _____

Poetry Collection: Jack Prelutsky, Rosemary and Stephen Vincent Benét, Ogden Nash

Support for Extend Your Learning

Research and Technology

For this assignment, you will use the Internet and other sources to gather a variety of poems and stories about dinosaurs, as well as illustrations. Then, you will organize those materials in a **booklet**. Use this chart to draft your booklet's annotations—the descriptive comments about each poem or story. Be sure each annotation compares or contrasts the poem or story with "Ankylosaurus."

Poem or Story Title	Annotation

Listening and Speaking

Use the following chart as you plan an **interview** with one of the Wright brothers. As you do your research, fill in the chart.

Question	Category	Answer

© Pearson Education, Inc., publishing as Pearson Prentice Hall. All rights reserved.

Poetry Collection: Jack Prelutsky, Rosemary and Stephen Vincent Benét, Ogden Nash

Enrichment: Keys to Success

In the poem "Wilbur Wright and Orville Wright," the Wright brothers succeed because they show *determination*. They work hard, endure injuries, and keep trying until they have built the world's first successful airplane. In "Adventures of Isabel," Isabel succeeds in defeating a bear, a giant, a witch, and even a doctor. Isabel's key to success is *resourcefulness*. She can always think of a way to overcome obstacles and meet challenges. The Wrights and Isabel share another key to success: *self-confidence*. The Wrights patch each other up. They believe in themselves and in each other. Isabel does not worry, scream, or scurry. She stays calm as she works to defeat her enemies. Developing determination, resourcefulness, and self-confidence will help you succeed at whatever you attempt—in school, at home, or in your community.

A. DIRECTIONS: *On the lines below, suggest how you or another student might use* determination, resourcefulness, *and* self-confidence *to meet each challenge. In your answer, specify which quality would be most important in the situation, and describe the actions that should be taken to achieve success.*

1. A music group you like very much is giving a concert in your area in a few months. You have permission to go to the concert with an adult, but you need to raise the money to pay for the tickets.

   _____
   _____
   _____

2. You want to take part in your school's talent show. Many classmates—not just your friends—have told you that you have an excellent voice. You have never sung in front of a panel of judges or an audience. Just thinking about it makes you nervous.

   _____
   _____
   _____

B. DIRECTIONS: *Describe a challenging situation you have faced or can imagine yourself facing. (Use your imagination!) Explain how* determination, resourcefulness, *and/or* self-confidence *did (or would) help you succeed.*

_____
_____
_____
_____
_____

© Pearson Education, Inc., publishing as Pearson Prentice Hall. All rights reserved.

Poetry Collection: Jack Prelutsky, Rosemary and Stephen Vincent Benét, Ogden Nash

Selection Test A

Critical Reading *Identify the letter of the choice that best answers the question.*

____ 1. How many stressed syllables are in this line from "Ankylosaurus"?
Clankity Clankity Clankity Clank!
   A. one
   B. four
   C. eight
   D. ten

____ 2. What kind of creature is the Ankylosaurus?
   A. a monster
   B. a ghost
   C. a dinosaur
   D. a tank

____ 3. Which words from "Ankylosaurus" suggest how smart the creature is?
   A. built like a tank
   B. armored behind
   C. its minuscule mind
   D. four stubby legs

____ 4. In "Wilbur Wright and Orville Wright," Orville Wright complains,
"These birds are very <u>trying</u>, / I'm sick of hearing them cheep-cheep . . ."
What does the context, the words around it, suggest is the meaning of *trying*?
   A. annoying
   B. ambitious
   C. strange
   D. sick

____ 5. Which sentence best describes the brothers' relationship in "Wilbur Wright and Orville Wright"?
   A. They compete with each other.
   B. They encourage each other.
   C. They are always fighting.
   D. They enjoy traveling together.

© Pearson Education, Inc., publishing as Pearson Prentice Hall. All rights reserved.

____ 6. In these lines from "Wilbur Wright and Orville Wright," which word rhymes with *shop*?

> They ran a dusty little shop
> For bicycle-repairing,
> And bought each other soda-pop

A. For

B. repairing

C. bought

D. pop

____ 7. Which word is a context clue to the meaning of *ravenous*?

> The bear was hungry, the bear was <u>ravenous</u>

A. bear

B. hungry

C. was

D. ravenous

____ 8. What does a reader learn about Isabel from reading "Adventures of Isabel"?

A. Isabel is ill.

B. Isabel is smart.

C. Isabel does not worry.

D. Isabel does not have friends.

____ 9. In "Adventures of Isabel," how is the doctor different from Isabel's other enemies—the bear, the witch, and the giant?

A. He is nice to her.

B. He frightens her.

C. He gets killed.

D. He may be real.

____ 10. Which quality do Wilbur Wright, Orville Wright, and Isabel have in common?

A. shyness

B. ambition

C. sadness

D. confidence

____ 11. How are the poems "Ankylosaurus," "Wilbur Wright and Orville Wright," and "Adventures of Isabel" alike?

A. They are humorous.

B. They are about strange creatures.

C. They have a serious message.

D. They have no rhyme or rhythm.

© Pearson Education, Inc., publishing as Pearson Prentice Hall. All rights reserved.

Vocabulary and Grammar

____ 12. Which sentence uses the underlined vocabulary word *incorrectly*?

A. The bread was blue with mold, so surely it was <u>inedible</u>.

B. Everyone liked the <u>inedible</u> meal that my mother prepared.

C. Because the man was unjustly accused, he felt <u>rancor</u>.

D. Most people will feel some <u>rancor</u> when someone harms them.

____ 13. In which situation would a person most likely feel *ravenous*?

A. He or she is happy.

B. He or she is confused.

C. He or she has not eaten all day.

D. He or she is angry with a friend.

____ 14. What does the prefix *pre-* mean?

A. before

B. again

C. after

D. across

____ 15. How many nouns make up the compound subject in this simple sentence?

A bear and a witch were two of Isabel's enemies.

A. one

B. two

C. three

D. four

Essay

16. Of the three poems in this collection—"Ankylosaurus," "Wilbur Wright and Orville Wright," and "Adventures of Isabel"—which one do you think is the most humorous? In an essay, tell which poem you think is the funniest. Tell three things about the poem that you think are funny.

17. When you meet people who are successful, you might recognize that they have qualities like those of Isabel in "Adventures of Isabel" or the Wright brothers in "Wilbur Wright and Orville Wright." In an essay, tell about one quality that both Isabel and the Wright brothers have that makes them successful. Then, tell about two ways in which Isabel and the Wrights are different from each other.

© Pearson Education, Inc., publishing as Pearson Prentice Hall. All rights reserved.

Name _____ Date _____

Poetry Collection: Jack Prelutsky, Rosemary and Stephen Vincent Benét, Ogden Nash
Selection Test B

Critical Reading *Identify the letter of the choice that best completes the statement or answers the question.*

_____ 1. Which words rhyme in these lines from "Ankylosaurus"?
　　　　its hide was a fortress as sturdy as steel, / it tended to be an inedible meal
　　　　A. sturdy, steel
　　　　B. tended, inedible
　　　　C. steel, meal
　　　　D. was, as

_____ 2. In "Ankylosaurus," the creature's body
　　　　A. is weak.
　　　　B. has no tail.
　　　　C. is strong.
　　　　D. has large wings.

_____ 3. Which question helps you use context clues to figure out the meaning of the under-
　　　　lined word in this line from "Ankylosaurus"?
　　　　there wasn't a thing on its <u>minuscule</u> mind
　　　　A. Where does the poem take place?
　　　　B. What do I know about dinosaurs?
　　　　C. What is an Ankylosaurus?
　　　　D. Which words explain *minuscule*?

_____ 4. How many *stressed* syllables are in this line from "Ankylosaurus"?
　　　　nibbling on plants with a mouthful of pegs
　　　　A. one
　　　　B. two
　　　　C. four
　　　　D. six

_____ 5. How many *unstressed* syllables are in this line from "Wilbur Wright and Orville Wright"?
　　　　Said Orville Wright to Wilbur Wright
　　　　A. two
　　　　B. four
　　　　C. six
　　　　D. eight

_____ 6. Which word means the same as *trying* in the following context?
　　　　These birds are very <u>trying</u>. / I'm sick of hearing them cheep-cheep . . .
　　　　A. risky
　　　　B. striving
　　　　C. ambitious
　　　　D. annoying

© Pearson Education, Inc., publishing as Pearson Prentice Hall. All rights reserved.

_____ 7. How would the brothers' relationship in "Wilbur Wright and Orville Wright" best be described?

A. They compete with each other.

B. They encourage each other.

C. They criticize each other.

D. They sympathize with each other.

_____ 8. Which word rhymes with *kings* in these lines from "Wilbur Wright and Orville Wright"?

—And kingdoms may forget their kings / And dogs forget their bites,

But, not till Man forgets his wings, / Will men forget the Wrights.

A. kingdoms

B. bites

C. wings

D. Wrights

_____ 9. In these lines from "Adventures of Isabel," which words are context clues to the meaning of *cavernous*?

The bear was hungry, the bear was ravenous,

The bear's big mouth was cruel and <u>cavernous</u>.

A. The bear was hungry

B. the bear was ravenous

C. The bear's big mouth

D. was cruel and cavernous

_____ 10. In "Adventures of Isabel," Isabel washes her hands and straightens her hair before she deals with the bear. Based only on that information, Isabel may best be described as

A. determined.

B. neat.

C. brave.

D. patient.

_____ 11. The doctor is different from Isabel's other enemies—the bear, the witch, and the giant—in that

A. he is nice to her.

B. he frightens her.

C. he could be imaginary.

D. he could be real.

_____ 12. In "Adventures of Isabel," the only one of Isabel's enemies who survives is

A. the bear.

B. the witch.

C. the giant.

D. the doctor.

© Pearson Education, Inc., publishing as Pearson Prentice Hall. All rights reserved.

____ 13. "Ankylosaurus," "Wilbur Wright and Orville Wright," and "Adventures of Isabel" are alike in their
   A. use of humor.
   B. patterns of rhythm.
   C. context.
   D. message.

Vocabulary and Grammar

____ 14. Which sentence uses the underlined vocabulary word *incorrectly?*
   A. The <u>ravenous</u> bear wanted to eat Isabel.
   B. Ankylosaurus ate only <u>inedible</u> plants.
   C. The Wrights felt <u>ravenous</u> even after drinking soda-pop.
   D. Isabel enjoyed food that many people would have found <u>inedible</u>.

____ 15. In which situation would a person most likely feel *rancor?*
   A. He or she has been hugged.
   B. He or she has been encouraged.
   C. He or she has been insulted.
   D. He or she has been praised.

____ 16. How many nouns make up the compound subject in this simple sentence?

   An enormous bear, a wicked witch, a hideous giant, and a troublesome doctor met Isabel.

   A. four
   B. five
   C. seven
   D. eight

____ 17. Which sentence contains a compound subject?
   A. The Ankylosaurus was built like a tank.
   B. Wilbur Wright and Orville Wright invented an airplane.
   C. Ogden Nash wrote "Adventures of Isabel."
   D. I liked all the poems in this collection.

Essay

18. Of the three poems in this collection—"Ankylosaurus," "Wilbur Wright and Orville Wright," and "Adventures of Isabel"—which one do you think is the most humorous? In an essay, tell which poem you find the funniest, and explain why. Explain how the poem's rhyme and rhythm add to its humor.

19. "Ankylosaurus" describes a creature that lived in a long-ago world. Wilbur Wright and Orville Wright lived in the recent past, and Isabel has her adventures in a fantasy world. In an essay, point to at least one detail in each poem that tells you something about those worlds. Then, tell which world you think is described most successfully, and explain why.

© Pearson Education, Inc., publishing as Pearson Prentice Hall. All rights reserved.

Vocabulary Warm-up Word Lists

Study these words from the poems. Then, apply your knowledge to the activities that follow.

Word List A

clasp [KLASP] *n.* hold; grip
   During the rollercoaster ride, I kept a firm underline{clasp} on the safety bar.

maids [MAYDZ] *n.* women who do cleaning work
   We worked for one summer as underline{maids}, cleaning nearby homes.

might [MYT] *n.* strength, ability, or power
   Les pushed on the door with all his underline{might}, but he couldn't open it.

overhead [OH vuhr hed] *adv.* above; up in the sky
   Dark clouds floating underline{overhead} made me think it was going to rain.

spoil [SPOYL] *v.* wreck or ruin
   Writing a poor paper might underline{spoil} your chance of getting an A.

weep [WEEP] *v.* cry; shed tears
   Cutting onions always makes me underline{weep}.

Word List B

avow [uh VOW] *v.* promise; say in front of other people
   I am not afraid to underline{avow} that I still like my teddy bears.

charm [CHAHRM] *n.* object a person might carry to bring good luck
   Jake had a lucky underline{charm} in his pocket, and he thought it might help him do well in the big game.

parting [PAHRT ing] *n.* the act of leaving
   underline{Parting} from old friends was sad for Janice; she couldn't bear to leave them behind.

pitiless [PIT i lis] *adj.* cruel; with no sympathy
   She doesn't care that I'm hurt; look at her underline{pitiless} expression!

quantities [KWAHN tuh tees] *n.* amounts
   These underline{quantities} of food are too large. Who could eat all that?

sulkily [SUHL kuh lee] *adv.* in a way that shows unhappiness or a bad attitude
   Jennifer underline{sulkily} gave me the cookie, and I could see that she really didn't like sharing.

© Pearson Education, Inc., publishing as Pearson Prentice Hall. All rights reserved.

Name _____ Date _____

Poetry Collection: Edgar Allan Poe, Maya Angelou, and Lewis Carroll
Vocabulary Warm-up Exercises

Exercise A *Fill in each blank in the paragraph below with an appropriate word from Word List A. Use each word only once.*

Lars ripped the flyer out of his sister's [1] _____. "Don't call us

[2] _____," he said. "Nico and I are cleaning professionals. If you use

the wrong word, it will [3] _____ our ad. No one will hire us!"

Lars and Nico hoped to make money by cleaning houses. They were trying with all

their [4] _____ to save money for a trip to Mexico.

"If we don't get to go," said Lars, "I think I will just break down and

[5] _____."

   "Don't worry," said Nico. "People will call us up and give us work. Pretty soon we'll be

on one of those planes flying [6] _____. I'm sure we will earn the money

we need."

Exercise B *Revise each sentence so that the underlined vocabulary word is used in a logical way. Be sure to keep the vocabulary word in your revision.*

Example: If you are not more <u>careful</u>, you might help yourself.
   If you are not more <u>careful</u>, you might hurt yourself.

1. Some people carry a rabbit's foot as a lucky <u>charm</u> to make sure bad things happen.

   _____

2. It was Bob's first time away from home, so <u>parting</u> from his family was easy.

   _____

3. Sheila is a <u>pitiless</u> person; she feels terrible if anyone else is unhappy.

   _____

4. My sister jumped up and down <u>sulkily</u> because she was happy with her gift.

   _____

5. Why did you bring me such large <u>quantities</u>? I told you I needed a lot.

   _____

6. At a wedding, the bride and the groom <u>avow</u> their dislike for each other.

   _____

Poetry Collection: Edgar Allan Poe, Maya Angelou, and Lewis Carroll
Reading Warm-up A

Read the following passage. Pay special attention to the underlined words. Then, read it again, and complete the activities. Use a separate sheet of paper for your written answers.

Pam's outdoor party was supposed to have been a happy event. Yet something went wrong that managed to spoil everything. What happened to ruin the party? Rex, Pam's pet cat, ran away.

It happened as her guests began to arrive. Pam was out in the backyard looking at the decorations. The whole yard was filled with lanterns lit by candles. Hanging overhead in the branches of the trees were orange and black streamers. Everyone was supposed to wear a costume. Pam's best friend, Tina, was dressed up as a pirate. Maya and Annie carried mops, brooms, and buckets. They were pretending to be maids.

Pam had brought Rex out to see her friends arrive, and as usual, she had a firm clasp on her pet. She liked to keep a good hold on Rex whenever she carried him outside. Suddenly, however, Rex leapt out of her arms and ran into the bushes that separated Pam's house from the neighboring yard.

Pam screamed, and everyone ran after the cat, trying to help Pam find him. Rex was gone, however. Despite everyone's help, her pet was nowhere to be seen. Pam began to weep. No matter how hard she tried, she couldn't keep the tears from flowing. With the host so unhappy, none of the party guests could enjoy themselves either. Soon, everyone went home.

A day passed, and another, and finally a whole week. There was no sign of Rex. Pam tried to get over her sadness, but it was difficult. Pam's mother promised to get her a new pet, but Pam knew it wouldn't be the same.

Then, late one night, two weeks after the party, Pam heard a familiar sound, a hushed meow. "It's Rex," Pam screamed with all her might. She ran to the backdoor where her lost pet was waiting to be let in.

1. Underline the nearby word that has the same meaning as spoil. Then, describe something else that might *spoil* an outdoor party.

2. Circle the words that tell what was hanging overhead. Then, tell what *overhead* means.

3. Circle the words that tell what helped Maya and Annie look like maids. Then, tell what *maids* do.

4. Circle the words that tell what Pam kept a clasp on. Then, tell what *clasp* means.

5. Underline the words that tell what Pam could not do when she started to weep. Then, describe something else that might make a person *weep*.

6. Underline the word that tells what Pam did with all her might. Then, tell what *might* means.

© Pearson Education, Inc., publishing as Pearson Prentice Hall. All rights reserved.

Poetry Collection: Edgar Allan Poe, Maya Angelou, and Lewis Carroll
Reading Warm-up B

Read the following passage. Pay special attention to the underlined words. Then, read it again, and complete the activities. Use a separate sheet of paper for your written answers.

It is important to feel confident about your abilities. It is important not to let life frighten you. Just because it is important, however, does not mean it is easy. Developing self-esteem, a good feeling about yourself and your abilities, can take some doing. Luckily, experts offer some advice that helps.

The secret, they say, is not carrying a good luck charm. Self-esteem is not a matter of luck. Instead, it involves finding something that you are good at and sticking with it. It might be drawing, or math, or playing sports, or volunteering to help others. It might be learning how to play an instrument. It could be tutoring younger kids in school. The activity is not what is important. The key is proving to yourself that you really do have great quantities of talent. Everybody has a great amount of talent; the question is simply figuring out how to develop it.

If you do not do well at something at first, do not give up and sulkily run away. Although parting may seem easier than staying, you will not feel better in the end. Instead, keep trying. In time, you may surprise yourself with newfound skills. Often, what keeps people from sticking to an activity is an unwillingness to ask questions.

Never be afraid to ask for help, the experts say. Most people are not pitiless and cruel; they do care about others. They are happy to share their knowledge and experience. If you ask someone to help you learn to do something, most of the time he or she will say yes. You will discover that they are eager to show you how something is done.

Avow out loud that in the future, you will not be afraid to try new activities or ask others for help. Pretty soon, you will discover where your talents are, and your self-esteem will soar.

1. Underline the words that tell what a charm is supposed to bring. Then, name something some people use as a *charm*.

2. Circle the nearby word that has nearly the same meaning as quantities. Then, use *quantities* in a sentence.

3. Circle the words that tell what a person might do when acting sulkily. Then, tell what *sulkily* means.

4. Underline the nearby word that means the opposite of parting. Then, tell what *parting* means.

5. Underline the nearby word that has nearly the same meaning as pitiless. Then, use the word *pitiless* in a sentence.

6. Underline the words that tell what you should avow out loud. Then, tell what *avow* means.

© Pearson Education, Inc., publishing as Pearson Prentice Hall. All rights reserved.

Name _____ Date _____

Poetry Collection: Maya Angelou, Edgar Allan Poe, Lewis Carroll
Reading: Ask Questions to Use Context Clues

When you come across a word you do not know or a word used in an unusual way, you can sometimes figure out the meaning by using context clues. **Context clues** are found in the words, phrases, and sentences surrounding an unfamiliar word. They may be words that have the same meaning or that describe or explain the word. To use context clues, **ask questions** such as these:

- *What kind of word is it?*
- *What word can I use in place of it?*
- *Which other words in the sentence explain it?*

DIRECTIONS: *Use this chart to figure out the meaning of some words that you may not know or that are used in an unusual way in the poems in this collection. For each item, write the question you would ask to figure out the meaning of the underlined word or words. Then, answer the question. Finally, write the meaning of the word or expression. The first item has been done for you.*

Word in Context	Question	Answer	Meaning
1. <u>Panthers</u> in the park / Strangers in the dark / No, they don't frighten me at all.	What kind of word is it?	It is a word that names an animal that frightens people.	kind of scary animal
2. Thus much let me <u>avow</u>— / You are not wrong			
3. I hold . . . / Grains of the golden sand— / How few! yet how they creep / Through my fingers to the <u>deep</u>			
4. can I not <u>grasp</u> / Them with a tighter clasp?			
5. The sun was shining on the sea, / . . . He did his very best to make / The <u>billows</u> smooth and bright			

© Pearson Education, Inc., publishing as Pearson Prentice Hall. All rights reserved.

Poetry Collection: Maya Angelou, Edgar Allan Poe, Lewis Carroll
Literary Analysis: Rhythm and Rhyme

Poets often use **rhythm** and **rhyme** to add a musical quality to their poems. **Rhythm** is the sound pattern created by stressed and unstressed syllables. Stressed syllables receive more emphasis than unstressed syllables. In this example, capital letters indicate the stressed syllables:)

The WAL-rus AND the CAR-pen-TER (4 stressed syllables, 4 unstressed syllables)

Were WALK-ing CLOSE at HAND (3 stressed syllables, 3 unstressed syllables)

Rhyme is the repetition of sounds at the ends of words, such as *wall* and *hall.* Once a rhyme pattern, or rhyme scheme, has been established, you come to expect the upcoming rhymes. Many traditional poems have rhyming words at the ends of lines.

DIRECTIONS: *Rewrite each of the following lines from the poems to show their rhythm and rhyme. Write each syllable separately, as in the example above. Use capital letters to show stressed syllables. Then, circle the words that rhyme.*

1. Don't show me frogs and snakes / And listen for my scream, /
   If I'm afraid at all / It's only in my dreams.

   _____

   _____

   _____

   _____

2. *All* that we see or seem / Is but a dream within a dream.

   _____

   _____

3. "The time has come," the Walrus said, / "To talk of many things: /
   Of shoes—and ships—and sealing wax— / Of cabbages—and kings—"

   _____

   _____

   _____

   _____

© Pearson Education, Inc., publishing as Pearson Prentice Hall. All rights reserved.

Poetry Collection: Maya Angelou, Edgar Allan Poe, Lewis Carroll
Vocabulary Builder

Word List

deem	quantities	beseech	dismal

A. DIRECTIONS: *Write the word from the Word List that best completes each sentence.*

1. My neighbor, a poet, said she would not _____ her barking dogs to be quiet.

2. Large _____ of salt and sugar were used to brine the oysters.

3. After five days of _____ weather, we were ready for a sunny day.

4. The editors _____ the excellent poem worthy of publication.

B. DIRECTIONS: *On each line, write the letter of the word that means* the same as *the word from the Word List.*

___ 1. deem
   A. taste   B. retreat   C. consider   D. march

___ 2. quantities
   A. amounts   B. questions   C. achievements   D. grades

___ 3. beseech
   A. pity   B. complain   C. destroy   D. beg

___ 4. dismal
   A. cute   B. gloomy   C. cheery   D. late

© Pearson Education, Inc., publishing as Pearson Prentice Hall. All rights reserved.

Name _____ Date _____

Support for Writing a Letter to an Author

Use this form to draft a **letter to the author** of "Life Doesn't Frighten Me," "A Dream Within a Dream," or "The Walrus and the Carpenter." Be sure to state your reaction to the poem and tell whether or not you like the poem. Include reasons for your reaction, and refer to the poem to support your reasons.

Heading: Your address and the date _____

_____

_____

_____

Inside Address: Where the letter will be sent _____

_____

_____

Greeting   Dear _____,

Begin **body** of letter. *State your over-all reaction.* _____

_____

_____

State reasons for your reaction, and give examples to support reasons. _____

_____

_____

_____

_____

_____

_____

_____

_____

_____

Closing and **Signature** _____

_____

Now, write a final draft of your letter to the author of one of the poems in this collection.

© Pearson Education, Inc., publishing as Pearson Prentice Hall. All rights reserved.

Poetry Collection: Maya Angelou, Edgar Allan Poe, Lewis Carroll
Support for Extend Your Learning

Research and Technology

For this assignment, you will use the Internet and other sources to gather a variety of poems and stories by Lewis Carroll, as well as illustrations. Then, you will organize those materials in a **booklet.** Use this chart to draft your booklet's annotations—the descriptive comments about each poem or story. Be sure each annotation compares or contrasts the poem or story with "The Walrus and the Carpenter."

Poem or Story Title	Annotation

Listening and Speaking

Use the following chart as you plan an **interview** with Maya Angelou, Edgar Allan Poe, or Lewis Carroll. As you do your research, fill in the chart.

Question	Category	Answer

© Pearson Education, Inc., publishing as Pearson Prentice Hall. All rights reserved.

Name _____ Date _____

Poetry Collection: Maya Angelou, Edgar Allan Poe, Lewis Carroll
Enrichment: Science and Nonsense

"The Walrus and the Carpenter" has been called a masterpiece of nonsense literature. Part of the humor in the poem comes from the fact that most of what is said about oysters is nonsense.

A. DIRECTIONS: *Read the following scientific information about oysters. Then, explain why the lines from "The Walrus and the Carpenter" quoted below are nonsense.*

An oyster is a sea animal with a soft body inside a hard, two-part shell. The oyster usually keeps its shell slightly open. When an enemy comes near, it slams the shell shut. Oysters spend their lives underwater, mostly in one spot at the bottom of the ocean. They have no developed eyes, ears, nose, head, legs, or hands. They have no feet, or just one "reduced foot." An oyster breathes through its gills. It pulls in water and filters out algae, tiny sea plants that it eats. Oysters serve a valuable purpose to humans by filtering out pollutants in ocean water. Since prehistoric times oysters have served an even more valuable purpose: People eat them—raw or cooked. Some people love oysters; others dislike them intensely. Another scientific fact about oysters sounds like something from a fairy tale: When a grain of sand gets caught inside some kinds of oysters, the oyster coats the sand with a shiny material, eventually forming a pearl.

1. "The eldest Oyster winked his eye, / And shook his heavy head"

   Why this is nonsense: _____

2. "Their coats were brushed, their faces washed"

   Why this is nonsense: _____

B. DIRECTIONS: *Many poems, legends, myths, and fairy tales contain a reference to an impossible task. In "Rumpelstiltskin," for instance, a maiden is required to spin straw into gold. Answer the following questions about impossible tasks.*

1. In "The Walrus and the Carpenter," the Walrus weeps when he thinks about all the sand on the beach. What impossible task does he suggest?

   _____

   _____

2. Describe an impossible task that you have read about or seen in movies, or use your imagination to make up an impossible task. Tell who performs the task and what tools, if any, may be used to perform it.

   _____

   _____

3. Describe a task that seems impossible but might be *scientifically* possible someday.

   _____

   _____

   _____

© Pearson Education, Inc., publishing as Pearson Prentice Hall. All rights reserved.

Poetry Collections: Jack Prelutsky, Rosemary and Stephen Vincent Benét,
Ogden Nash; Maya Angelou, Edgar Allan Poe, Lewis Carroll

Build Language Skills: Vocabulary

Prefixes

When the prefix *pre-* is added to a word, it adds the meaning "before." For example, add *pre-* to the word *view*, meaning "to see or inspect." The result is *preview*, meaning "to view beforehand." Here are two more examples:

Before baking the cake, *preheat* the oven to 350 degrees.

If you want to be sure you will have a seat on that flight, *prepurchase* your ticket.

A. DIRECTIONS: *Follow the instructions to write sentences using words with the prefix* pre-.

1. Use *preflight* in a sentence about crew-member activities before takeoff.

_____

2. Use *preteens* in a sentence about activities that twelve-year-olds might enjoy.

_____

3. Use *prehistoric* in a sentence about animals that may have roamed Earth long ago.

_____

4. Use *precautionary* in a sentence about preparing for a rain storm.

_____

Academic Vocabulary Practice

B. DIRECTIONS: *Circle* T *if the statement is true or* F *if the statement is false. Then, explain your answer.*

1. A movie *preview* usually tells how the movie ends.

T / F _____

2. If someone asked you to *restate* a poem, you could do it in three words.

T / F _____

3. To figure out the meaning of an unfamiliar word from its *context*, you would look up the word in a dictionary.

T / F _____

4. To *define* an unfamiliar word, you would look up the word in an encyclopedia.

T / F _____

5. It would be easy to *explain* a nonsense poem.

T / F _____

© Pearson Education, Inc., publishing as Pearson Prentice Hall. All rights reserved.

Name _____ Date _____

Build Language Skills: Grammar

Sentences: Simple and Compound Subjects

A **sentence** is a group of words that has a subject and a verb and expresses a complete thought. A **simple sentence** expresses a single thought. It can contain a simple subject or a compound subject. A **subject** is the word or group of words that tells who or what the sentence is about. A **simple subject** is made up of one noun or pronoun. A **compound subject** is made up of two or more nouns or pronouns. The nouns or pronouns in a compound subject are connected by conjunctions such as *and, or,* or *nor.*

   Simple subject: <u>Spring</u> is my favorite season.
   Compound subject: <u>Spring</u>, <u>summer</u>, <u>winter</u>, and <u>fall</u> are the four seasons.

A. PRACTICE: *Underline the simple or compound subject in each sentence.*

1. Animals and people are good subjects for poems.
2. After dinner, will you or Robert put away the leftovers?
3. Everyone should come up with a plan.
4. Every spring, hungry deer and raccoons invade our garden in search of food.
5. On a counter in the kitchen, flour, sugar, and butter are waiting to be made into cookies.
6. Lewis Carroll may well be my favorite poet.

B. Writing Application: *If you could write a poem about any two subjects, what two subjects would you choose? In a brief paragraph, discuss the subjects you would use, and why. Include at least one sentence that has a simple subject and two sentences that have compound subjects. Underline the simple or compound subject in each sentence.*

_____

_____

_____

_____

_____

_____

_____

_____

_____

_____

© Pearson Education, Inc., publishing as Pearson Prentice Hall. All rights reserved.

Poetry Collection: Maya Angelou, Edgar Allan Poe, Lewis Carroll
Selection Test A

Critical Reading *Identify the letter of the choice that best answers the question.*

____ 1. In these four lines from "Life Doesn't Frighten Me," which word rhymes with *boo*?

I go boo / Make them shoo / I make fun / Way they run

A. go

B. shoo

C. fun

D. run

____ 2. In "Life Doesn't Frighten Me," where does the speaker say she or he may be afraid?

A. in the park

B. in dreams

C. on the ocean floor

D. at a new school

____ 3. In "Life Doesn't Frighten Me," what is the speaker's outstanding quality?

A. politeness

B. hopefulness

C. fear

D. self-confidence

____ 4. In this line from "A Dream Within a Dream," there are three unstressed syllables. How many *stressed* syllables are there?

Take this kiss upon the brow!

A. two

B. three

C. four

D. six

____ 5. What is happening at the beginning of "A Dream Within a Dream"?

A. Two people are parting.

B. Two people are falling in love.

C. Two people are meeting.

D. Two people are fighting.

© Pearson Education, Inc., publishing as Pearson Prentice Hall. All rights reserved.

Name _____ Date _____

____ **6.** Which word best describes how the speaker in "A Dream Within a Dream" feels?
  A. sad
  B. hopeful
  C. surprised
  D. scared

____ **7.** In these lines from "A Dream Within a Dream," the speaker dreams of holding a few grains of sand. What is the meaning of *creep* in this context?

  How few! yet how they <u>creep</u> / Through my fingers to the deep

  A. stick
  B. grow
  C. crawl
  D. slip

____ **8.** In "The Walrus and the Carpenter," why does the eldest Oyster not go with the Walrus and the Carpenter?
  A. He is too young.
  B. He is suspicious.
  C. He is not ready.
  D. He is busy eating.

____ **9.** In "The Walrus and the Carpenter," why do the Walrus and the Carpenter trick the young Oysters?
  A. to get them to exercise
  B. to play with them
  C. to eat them
  D. to teach them a lesson

____ **10.** In these lines from "The Walrus and the Carpenter," *thick* means "many and close together." Which words provide a context clue to that meaning?

  And <u>thick</u> and fast they came at last, / And more, and more, and more—

  A. and fast
  B. they came
  C. at last
  D. more, and more, and more

____ **11.** In the poems in this collection, who faces life with the most self-confidence?
  A. the Carpenter in "The Walrus and the Carpenter"
  B. the speaker in "Life Doesn't Frighten Me"
  C. the speaker in "A Dream Within a Dream"
  D. the Oysters in "The Walrus and the Carpenter"

Vocabulary and Grammar

___ **12.** Which sentence uses the underlined vocabulary word *incorrectly*?

    A. Voters <u>deem</u> her the best candidate.

    B. The <u>dismal</u> news was a joy to hear.

    C. The Oysters <u>beseech</u> the Walrus to stop.

    D. <u>Quantities</u> of plastic litter the beach.

___ **13.** What is the meaning of the word *prerecorded*?

    A. recorded again

    B. recorded thoroughly

    C. recorded afterward

    D. recorded beforehand

___ **14.** Which choice is a sentence—a group of words with a subject and a verb that expresses a complete thought?

    A. All alone at night.

    B. Not at all.

    C. To give a hand to each.

    D. They had eaten every one.

___ **15.** Which sentence contains a compound subject?

    A. The Walrus and the Carpenter walked along the beach.

    B. The Oysters were eager to have a treat.

    C. Lewis Carroll wrote "The Walrus and the Carpenter."

    D. They had a pleasant walk and a pleasant talk.

Essay

16. Which of the three poems in this collection—"Life Doesn't Frighten Me," "A Dream Within a Dream," or "The Walrus and the Carpenter"—do you like the best? In an essay, state your choice, and name two details from the poem that you especially enjoy. You might refer to ideas, scenes, rhythm patterns, or rhymes.

17. In "The Walrus and the Carpenter," a mean trick is played on the young Oysters. In an essay, describe how the Walrus and the Carpenter trick the Oysters. Then, state whether you think the poem is completely humorous. Does it make any serious point? If you think the poem makes a serious point, say what it is.

© Pearson Education, Inc., publishing as Pearson Prentice Hall. All rights reserved.

Name _____ Date _____

Selection Test B

Critical Reading *Identify the letter of the choice that best completes the statement or answers the question.*

_____ 1. Which question helps you figure out the meaning of the underlined word from "Life Doesn't Frighten Me"?

I go boo / Make them <u>shoo</u> / I make fun / Way they run

A. What is the poem about?
B. How does the speaker feel?
C. What kind of word is it?
D. Which word rhymes with it?

_____ 2. In these three lines from "Life Doesn't Frighten Me," which words rhyme most closely?

Panthers in the park / Strangers in the dark / No, they don't frighten me at all.

A. Panthers, park
B. Panthers, Strangers
C. park, dark
D. dark, all

_____ 3. The speaker in "Life Doesn't Frighten Me" says that Mother Goose, lions, and kissy little girls are alike in that
A. they do not frighten him or her.
B. only children fear them.
C. they are imaginary beings.
D. they make him or her laugh.

_____ 4. At the beginning of "A Dream Within a Dream," two people seem to be
A. falling in love for the first time.
B. parting from each other.
C. meeting after a long time.
D. talking about their dream.

_____ 5. Which words rhyme in these lines from "A Dream Within a Dream"?

Thus much let me avow—

You are not wrong, who deem

That my days have been a dream

A. avow, deem
B. avow, dream
C. deem, days
D. deem, dream

© Pearson Education, Inc., publishing as Pearson Prentice Hall. All rights reserved.

____ **6.** How many stressed syllables are in *each* line of these three lines from "A Dream Within a Dream"?

> Yet if hope has flown away / In a night, or in a day, / In a vision, or in none

A. two
B. three
C. four
D. seven

____ **7.** In "A Dream Within a Dream," which phrase is a context clue to the meaning of *grasp*?

> While I weep—while I weep! / O God! can I not <u>grasp</u> / Them with a tighter clasp?

A. While I weep
B. O God! can I not
C. can I not grasp them
D. with a tighter clasp

____ **8.** In "The Walrus and the Carpenter," the eldest Oyster will not go for a walk because it is
A. too hungry.
B. too suspicious.
C. busy sleeping.
D. busy eating.

____ **9.** The Walrus and the Carpenter trick the Oysters in order to
A. get them to walk.
B. play with them.
C. eat them.
D. teach them about life.

____ **10.** In these lines from "The Walrus and the Carpenter," *get it clear* means "remove the sand from it." Which words are a context clue to that meaning?

> "If seven maids with seven mops / Swept it for half a year,
>
> Do you suppose," the Walrus said, / "That they could <u>get it clear</u>?"

A. seven maids
B. Swept it
C. for half a year
D. Do you suppose

____ **11.** Which detail in "The Walrus and the Carpenter" is *not* an example of nonsense?
A. The sun is shining at night.
B. The Oysters can walk and talk.
C. The Walrus can talk.
D. The Carpenter says nothing.

____ **12.** How many stressed syllables are there in these lines?

> The sea was wet as wet could be, / The sands were dry as dry.

A. 4 in the first line, 3 in the second line
B. 4 in the first line, 4 in the second line
C. 4 in the first line, 6 in the second line
D. 3 in the first line, 6 in the second line

© Pearson Education, Inc., publishing as Pearson Prentice Hall. All rights reserved.

_____ 13. In the poems in this collection, who faces life with the most hopefulness and self-confidence?
A. the speaker in "Life Doesn't Frighten Me"
B. the speaker in "A Dream Within a Dream"
C. the Oysters in "The Walrus and the Carpenter"
D. the Walrus in "The Walrus and the Carpenter"

Vocabulary and Grammar

_____ 14. Which sentence uses the underlined vocabulary word *incorrectly?*
A. The dismal news was welcomed by everyone.
B. The judges deem her poems to be the best.
C. The Oysters beseech the Walrus to stop.
D. Quantities of sand were taken from the beach.

_____ 15. The word *caution* means "carefulness." *Precaution* means
A. being uncertain.
B. serving as an example.
C. being extra careful.
D. care taken in advance.

_____ 16. Which sentence contains a compound subject?
A. Maya Angelou is the author of "Life Doesn't Frighten Me."
B. Bad dogs and big ghosts do not frighten the speaker in "Life Doesn't Frighten Me."
C. I like "A Dream Within a Dream" better than "Life Doesn't Frighten Me."
D. The Oysters walk and talk with the Walrus and the Carpenter.

_____ 17. How many nouns make up the subject of this sentence?
The Walrus, the Carpenter, and the four young Oysters walked together on the beach.

A. two
B. three
C. four
D. five

Essay

18. Choose one of the poems in this collection—"Life Doesn't Frighten Me," "A Dream Within a Dream," or "The Walrus and the Carpenter." In an essay, describe the kind of person you think the speaker of the poem might be. Support your ideas about the speaker with three clues from the poem. Include clues that suggest whether the speaker is male or female.

19. Some people see life as an adventure and look forward to the future. Other people worry about the future. Consider the speakers in "Life Doesn't Frighten Me" and "A Dream Within a Dream." In an essay, tell whether each speaker is hopeful or fearful. Use two clues from each poem to support your opinion.

© Pearson Education, Inc., publishing as Pearson Prentice Hall. All rights reserved.

Vocabulary Warm-up Word Lists

Study these words from the poetry of Eve Merriam, Emily Dickinson, and Langston Hughes. Then, apply your knowledge to the activities that follow.

Word List A

chorus [KAWR uhs] *n.* a part of a song sung by many voices at once
Early in the morning, all the birds in the forest sang together in a <u>chorus</u> of chirping.

delicate [DEL i kit] *adj.* finely made or sensitive
The old dress was made out of <u>delicate</u> fabric that was easily torn.

pools [POOLZ] *n.* small, deep areas of water that sit in one place instead of flowing somewhere
After the storm, the street was covered in <u>pools</u> of rainwater.

silken [SILK uhn] *adj.* very smooth and soft, like silk
The texture of Laura's hair was <u>silken</u>.

sketch [SKECH] *n.* a quick, rough drawing of something
The artist quickly drew a <u>sketch</u> of the tree he planned to paint.

streaming [STREEM ing] *v.* moving or flowing steadily
During the storm, the rain came <u>streaming</u> down.

Word List B

fame [FAYM] *n.* the state or quality of being well known
The actor found <u>fame</u> after starring in many popular movies.

gutter [GUHT uhr] *n.* a pipe on a house or a ditch at the side of a road for carrying away rainwater
Anna fell on the side of the road and landed in a puddle in the <u>gutter</u>.

liquid [LIK wid] *adj.* wet and free-flowing, like water
The melting ice turned <u>liquid</u>, and a puddle began to form around it.

precious [PRESH uhs] *adj.* rare and valuable
Because she was always busy, Gina thought her free time was <u>precious</u>.

sting [STING] *n.* a small painful wound, such as one caused by a bee
The bee's <u>sting</u> was sharp and painful.

worthy [WER thee] *adj.* deserving of or good enough for
Tony worked hard to be <u>worthy</u> of his teacher's praise.

© Pearson Education, Inc., publishing as Pearson Prentice Hall. All rights reserved.

Name _____ Date _____

Poetry Collection: Eve Merriam, Emily Dickinson, and Langston Hughes
Vocabulary Warm-up Exercises

Exercise A *Fill in each blank in the paragraph below with an appropriate word from Word List A. Use each word only once.*

Johnny loved to walk through the fields after the rain. Bullfrogs gathered near the newly

formed [1] _____ of water. Their croaking sounded like the

[2] _____ of a song. The cool breeze went [3] _____

through the grass, steadily bending it. Each small and [4] _____ blade of

grass bent in the wind. As he leaned down to touch the new grass, it felt as

[5] _____ as the fine hair on his sister's head. Johnny decided that one

day he would bring his charcoal pencils and make a [6] _____ of the

fields after the rain.

Exercise B *Decide whether each statement below is true or false. Circle T or F, then explain your answers.*

1. Jumping into a puddle in a <u>gutter</u> will make you cleaner.
   T / F _____

2. After being covered with <u>liquid</u>, a person will feel dry.
   T / F _____

3. Something that is <u>precious</u> is rare and hard to come by.
   T / F _____

4. A wasp, like a bee, has a <u>sting</u>.
   T / F _____

5. Someone who works hard is <u>worthy</u> of a reward.
   T / F _____

6. If a person has <u>fame</u>, it means that no one recognizes them.
   T / F _____

© Pearson Education, Inc., publishing as Pearson Prentice Hall. All rights reserved.

Name _____ Date _____

Read the following passage. Pay special attention to the underlined words. Then, read it again, and complete the activities. Use a separate sheet of paper for your written answers.

Have you ever seen a weeping willow tree? Weeping willow trees often grow near small bodies of water, like <u>pools</u> or ponds. This type of tree is easy to recognize. It has long, <u>delicate</u> branches and thin leaves. These fine and fragile branches hang low to the ground.

Weeping willows are praised for their appearance. These trees are called "weeping" because they appear to be bent over, crying into the water. In the spring, the leaves of the weeping willow are a gentle pale green. Then they turn yellow in the fall. Willows also have flowers. The flowers start out as soft, shiny buds. As they grow, however, these <u>silken</u> buds open to the golden pollen inside.

The thin branches of the weeping willow tree blow easily in the wind. Wind <u>streaming</u> through the trees makes the branches bend and sway. The sound of the wind blowing steadily through the branches is lovely. As the branches hit each other, they make a rustling noise. On a windy day, the noise of the wind in the branches can sound like the <u>chorus</u> of a song.

The wood of willow trees can be used to make many things. For example, willow tree wood pulp is used to make paper. Willow paper is well known among artists. It is very easy to draw a <u>sketch</u> on this type of paper. It catches many of the details of an artist's rough drawing.

Weeping willows originally grew in Europe. Now, weeping willows can be found all over the world. They grow in many different areas of the United States. Because they are beautiful, they are planted in many parks. Perhaps a weeping willow grows in a park near you.

1. Underline the words that explain what <u>pools</u> are. Then, describe *pools* in your own words.

2. Circle the words in the next sentence that hint at the meaning of <u>delicate</u>. Then, tell about something that you think is *delicate*.

3. Circle the nearby words that tell you what <u>silken</u> means. Then, use the word *silken* in a sentence.

4. Underline the words that tell what the <u>streaming</u> wind does to the willow's branches. Then, tell what *streaming* means.

5. Underline the words that tell you what can sound like a <u>chorus</u>. Then, write a sentence using the word *chorus*.

6. Circle the words that describe what a <u>sketch</u> is. Explain why an artist might make a *sketch* of a scene before painting it.

© Pearson Education, Inc., publishing as Pearson Prentice Hall. All rights reserved.

Poetry Collection: Eve Merriam, Emily Dickinson, and Langston Hughes
Reading Warm-up B

Read the following passage. Pay special attention to the underlined words. Then, read it again, and complete the activities. Use a separate sheet of paper for your written answers.

As Rita stepped out of the movie theater, she realized it was raining. As a matter of fact, it had started to pour. Rita sadly realized that she had left her umbrella at home. She groaned, knowing that soon she would be very wet. The cool, <u>liquid</u> drops of rain began to soak Rita's hair and clothing, running down her neck and her shoulders.

Because it had started to rain very suddenly, many people on the street did not have their umbrellas with them. Only a small number of people carried them. Rita looked around at these few, <u>precious</u> umbrellas. It would be so valuable to have one now!

She tried to distract herself from the fact that she was getting very wet. She thought of the movie she had just watched, which had been a comedy starring her favorite actress. Rita imagined that she, Rita, was well known, like the actress. "If I had <u>fame</u> like that," she thought to herself, "I bet someone would recognize me and give me their umbrella."

Her daydream was rudely interrupted when a car drove very quickly through a puddle in the <u>gutter</u> by the side of the road. Water splashed up from the puddle and soaked Rita's jeans. The cold beads of water hit Rita's legs. Each drop was so small and sharp that it felt like the <u>sting</u> of a bee.

Knowing that she wasn't far from her house, Rita broke into a run. She couldn't wait to get inside so that she could relax in a nice, warm bath. With her destination in mind, Rita ran as fast as her legs would take her. When she passed through her doorway, she felt the comforting heat of her house. After getting so wet, she felt <u>worthy</u> of the long bath she was about to take. After being soaked in the rain, she felt that she deserved to spend her afternoon pampering herself.

1. Underline the words that tell what the <u>liquid</u> drops of rain do to Rita. What is something you would describe as *liquid*?

2. Circle the words that help to explain what <u>precious</u> means. Then, write a sentence using the word *precious*.

3. Underline the words that tell what a person who has <u>fame</u> is like. Explain whether *fame* is something you would like to have.

4. Underline the words that describe the location of the <u>gutter</u>. Then, write a sentence using the word *gutter*.

5. Circle the words that describe what a <u>sting</u> feels like. Then, tell what a *sting* is.

6. Underline the sentence that tells why Rita felt <u>worthy</u> of a long bath. Name two things that might make a person *worthy* of special treatment.

© Pearson Education, Inc., publishing as Pearson Prentice Hall. All rights reserved.

Poetry Collection: Eve Merriam, Emily Dickinson, Langston Hughes
Reading: Reread and Read Ahead to Find and Use Context Clues

Context is the situation in which a word or an expression is used. The words and phrases in the surrounding text give you clues to the meaning of the word. Sometimes a word has more than one meaning. You may recognize a word but not recognize the way in which it is used. **Reread and read ahead** to find and use context clues that clarify meanings of words with multiple meanings. Look at the following examples to see how context clarifies the meaning of *dips:*

The willow <u>dips</u> to the water. (*Dips* is an action the tree takes to reach the water.)

At the party we tasted the many delicious <u>dips</u>. (*Dips* are something one eats at a party.)

As you read the poems, notice words that are used in unfamiliar or unusual ways. Use the context to help determine the meaning of the words.

DIRECTIONS: *Study the underlined word in each of the following lines from "Simile: Willow and Ginkgo" or "April Rain Song." Look for context clues in the lines that hint at the meaning of the word. On the line, write the context clues. Then, write two meanings for the word—first the meaning that fits the context, and then a meaning that does not fit the context. The first item has been done for you.*

1. "The willow is like a nymph with <u>streaming</u> hair"

    Context clues: <u>"like a nymph," "hair"</u> _____

    Meaning in context: <u>long, flowing</u>   **Second meaning:** <u>moving quickly</u>

2. "Wherever it grows, there is green and gold and <u>fair</u>."

    Context clues: _____

    Meaning in context: _____ **Second meaning:** _____

3. "Let the rain beat upon your head with <u>silver</u> liquid drops."

    Context clues: _____

    Meaning in context: _____ **Second meaning:** _____

4. "The rain makes <u>still</u> pools on the sidewalk."

    Context clues: _____

    Meaning in context: _____ **Second meaning:** _____

Poetry Collection: Eve Merriam, Emily Dickinson, Langston Hughes
Literary Analysis: Figurative Language

Figurative language is language that is not meant to be taken literally. Authors use figurative language to state ideas in fresh ways. They may use one or more of the following types of figurative language:

- **Similes** compare two different things using the word *like* or *as:* "The ginkgo is like a crude sketch."
- **Metaphors** compare two different things by stating that one thing is another: "Fame is a bee."
- **Personification** compares an object or animal to a human by giving it human characteristics: "Let the rain sing you a lullaby."

A. DIRECTIONS: *Underline each example of figurative language. Above it, write S if it is a simile, M if it is a metaphor, and P if it is personification.*

It began to drizzle as I walked home. <u>The rain tapped me on the shoulder</u>. Gentle rain-
drops fell like flower petals on my head and shoulders. The soft downpour was a surprising
gift. I had been working like a machine, trying to finish my homework, and now the shower
was a kindly messenger telling me to forget my worries.

B. DIRECTIONS: *In this chart, identify the type of figurative language. Then, tell what it does and what it shows. Look back at the poem if you need more context.*

Figurative Language	Type	What It Does	What It Shows
1. The willow is like a nymph with streaming hair ("Simile: Willow and Ginkgo")	simile	It compares branches to hair.	It shows that the branches are long.
2. Like a city child, it grows up in the street. ("Simile: Willow and Ginkgo")			
3. the metal sky ("Simile: Willow and Ginkgo")			
4. Let the rain kiss you ("April Rain Song")			

© Pearson Education, Inc., publishing as Pearson Prentice Hall. All rights reserved.

Poetry Collection: Eve Merriam, Emily Dickinson, Langston Hughes
Vocabulary Builder

Word List

> chorus   thrives

A. DIRECTIONS: *Read the incomplete paragraph below. On each line, write one of the words from the Word List. You will use each word twice. Think about the meaning of the word in the context of the paragraph.*

We walk in a park at night. The trunk of a birch tree shines in the moonlight. A
[1] _____ of frogs croaks its greetings from the stream. A snake is one
creature that [2] _____ here because it has few natural enemies. We
have seen it slithering through the grass. It [3] _____ on the many small
animals that come out only at night. As we leave the park, if we listen closely, we can
hear a [4] _____ of crickets singing good-bye.

B. DIRECTIONS: *Think about the meaning of the underlined word in each item below. Then, answer the question, and explain your answer.*

1. If someone were a member of a <u>chorus</u>, would he or she sing alone or with a group?

   _____

   _____

2. Which animal <u>thrives</u> in the company of humans, a bear or a dog?

   _____

   _____

C. DIRECTIONS: *Write the letter of the group of words whose meaning is* most nearly the same *as that of the word from the Word List.*

____ 1. chorus
   A. list of chores
   B. group of singers
   C. group of frogs
   D. group of musical tones

____ 2. thrives
   A. grows well
   B. improves slightly
   C. cries softly
   D. beats rhythmically

© Pearson Education, Inc., publishing as Pearson Prentice Hall. All rights reserved.

Poetry Collection: Eve Merriam, Emily Dickinson, Langston Hughes
Support for Writing a Poem With Figurative Language

Use this cluster diagram to gather ideas for a **poem** you will write using figurative language. First, write your subject in the oval at the center of the diagram. Then, in each circle around the oval, jot down one quality of your subject. Add more circles if you need them.

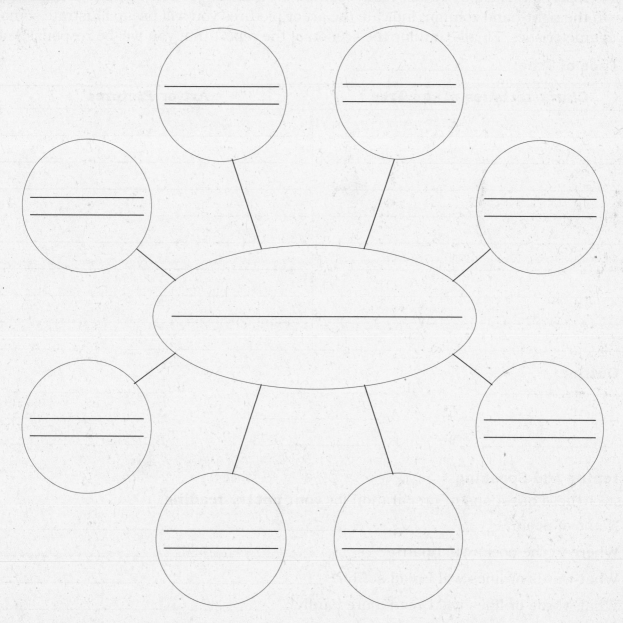

Now, use your notes to draft your poem. Be sure your poem has at least one simile, metaphor, or personification.

© Pearson Education, Inc., publishing as Pearson Prentice Hall. All rights reserved.

Poetry Collection: Eve Merriam, Emily Dickinson, Langston Hughes
Support for Extend Your Learning

Research and Technology

Use this chart as you work with a group of classmates to prepare a **multimedia report** on characteristics of a tree that grows in your community. First, identify the kind of tree you plan to report on. Then, in the left-hand column of the chart, jot down characteristics of the tree. In the right-hand column, indicate the art or pictures you will use to illustrate some of the characteristics. Finally, outline the section of the report that you will be responsible for.

Type of Tree: _____

Characteristics of the Tree	Art or Pictures

Outline:

I. _____   II. _____   III. _____

　A. _____   　A. _____   　A. _____

　B. _____   　B. _____   　B. _____

Listening and Speaking

Answer these questions in preparation for your **poetry reading.**

Name of poem: _____

Where in the poem will I pause? _____

What words or lines will I read softly? _____

What words or lines will I read more loudly? _____

At what points in the poem will I show strong emotion? How should I read those parts?

_____

_____

Which words should I stress for effect? _____

_____

© Pearson Education, Inc., publishing as Pearson Prentice Hall. All rights reserved.

Name _____ Date _____

Enrichment: Science

Eve Merriam's poem "Simile: Willow and Ginkgo" contrasts just two kinds of trees. There are many more kinds of trees, each with its own characteristics. Below are descriptions of the six main groups of trees. Notice that ginkgo trees are a single species.

Broadleaf trees are the most varied. There are more broadleaf trees in the world than any other type of tree. They include most trees found in North America. Broadleaf trees have flat leaves that change color in the fall and drop off in the winter. Some broadleaf trees have thick branches; others have slender branches that hang down.

Needle-leaf trees have needlelike leaves. Pines and redwoods belong in this group. Most needle-leaf trees are evergreen. They bear their seeds in cones.

Palm trees grow mainly in the tropics. Most have large leaves and no branches.

Cycad trees live in warm, wet regions. They look like palm trees but are most closely related to pines. Their cones may grow to be three feet long.

Tree ferns also look much like palms, but they reproduce by means of spores.

Ginkgo trees are one of the oldest species of tree, dating back millions of years. The ginkgo can live in almost any environment. Ginkgoes even grow between the cracks of city sidewalks, where there is barely enough soil for any plant to take root. Ginkgoes have fan-shaped leaves. Their seeds have an unpleasant odor.

A. DIRECTIONS: *Use the information above and from your reading of "Simile: Willow and Ginkgo" to answer the following questions.*

1. To what group of trees does the willow belong? Include three facts to support your answer.

_____

_____

_____

2. Name one fact mentioned in the descriptions above that Merriam refers to in her poem.

_____

_____

B. DIRECTIONS: *Find pictures of a willow and a ginkgo in a book about trees, in an encyclopedia, or on the Internet. In the space below, draw and label each tree and its leaf. Use a separate sheet of paper if you need more space.*

© Pearson Education, Inc., publishing as Pearson Prentice Hall. All rights reserved.

Poetry Collection: Eve Merriam, Emily Dickinson, Langston Hughes

Selection Test A

Critical Reading *Identify the letter of the choice that best answers the question.*

____ 1. Which statement best describes the two trees in "Simile: Willow and Ginkgo"?
A. The willow and the ginkgo look alike.
B. The willow is shorter than the ginkgo.
C. The willow has stubby branches; the ginkgo has long, silky branches.
D. The willow is delicate and beautiful; the ginkgo is tough and strong.

____ 2. Which line in "Simile: Willow and Ginkgo" contains a simile?
A. "The willow is like an etching."
B. "The willow dips to the water."
C. "Thrust against the metal sky"
D. "Somehow it survives and even thrives."

____ 3. When you read ahead to find context clues, which word suggests the best meaning for *crude* in this line from "Simile: Willow and Ginkgo"?
    The ginkgo is like a crude sketch, / Hardly worthy to be signed.
A. delicate
B. sleek
C. rough
D. precious

____ 4. What is the meaning of this line from "Simile: Willow and Ginkgo"?
    But my heart goes to the ginkgo.
A. I dislike the ginkgo.
B. I prefer the ginkgo.
C. I will plant a ginkgo.
D. I prefer the willow.

____ 5. Which statement tells you what the speaker in "Fame Is a Bee" thinks about Fame?
A. Everyone should seek it.
B. It has both good and bad points.
C. Everyone should try to avoid it.
D. Nobody has control over it.

© Pearson Education, Inc., publishing as Pearson Prentice Hall. All rights reserved.

_____ 6. The speaker in "Fame Is a Bee" says that Fame is like a bee because it has all that a bee has except for one thing. What is Fame missing?

    A. a sting

    B. a song

    C. a queen

    D. a wing

_____ 7. Which figure of speech is illustrated by this line from Emily Dickinson's poem?

    Fame is a bee.

    A. a simile using the word *like*

    B. a simile using the word *as*

    C. a metaphor

    D. personification

_____ 8. Which line from "April Rain Song" contains personification?

    A. "Let the rain sing you a lullaby."

    B. "The rain makes still pools on the sidewalk."

    C. "The rain makes running pools in the gutter."

    D. "And I love the rain."

_____ 9. Which words in "April Rain Song" provide the best context clue to the correct meaning of *plays* as it is used in this line?

    The rain <u>plays</u> a little sleep-song on our roof at night—

    A. the rain

    B. a little sleep-song

    C. on our roof

    D. at night

_____ 10. Which word describes how the speaker in "April Rain Song" feels about rain?

    A. worried

    B. angry

    C. sad

    D. loving

_____ 11. What is one way in which "Simile: Willow and Ginkgo," "Fame Is a Bee," and "April Rain Song" are alike?

    A. They use rhyme and rhythm.

    B. They are humorous.

    C. They use figurative language.

    D. They are sad and hopeless.

© Pearson Education, Inc., publishing as Pearson Prentice Hall. All rights reserved.

Vocabulary and Grammar

___ 12. Which sentence uses the underlined vocabulary word *incorrectly*?
   A. Everyone joined in a <u>chorus</u> of good-byes.
   B. Carlos is the only person in the school <u>chorus</u>.
   C. A ginkgo tree <u>thrives</u> in almost any climate.
   D. Our business <u>thrives</u> because we have few expenses.

___ 13. What is the meaning of the prefix *re-*, as in the word *renew*?
   A. more or less
   B. before or after
   C. to or from
   D. back or again

___ 14. When you *restate* a sentence, what do you do?
   A. You say it again.
   B. You disagree with it.
   C. You summarize it.
   D. You write it down.

___ 15. Which of these sentences is interrogative?
   A. It survives and even thrives.
   B. What a beautiful tree!
   C. Do you love the rain?
   D. Do not let fame sting you.

Essay

16. Choose one of the poems in this collection—"Simile: Willow and Ginkgo," "Fame Is a Bee," or "April Rain Song." In an essay, tell how you think the speaker of that poem feels about the subject of the poem—two trees, fame, or rain. Then, describe how you feel about the subject. Tell whether you agree or disagree with the speaker. Give two reasons for your answer. Base your reasons on your own experience or knowledge of trees or fame or rain.

17. Which of the poems in this collection—"Simile: Willow and Ginkgo," "Fame Is a Bee," or "April Rain Song"—do you like best? Write an essay about one of the poems. First, tell what you like about what the poet says. Then, tell what you like about the language of the poem. Give an example of one figure of speech—a simile, a metaphor, or personification that you especially liked.

© Pearson Education, Inc., publishing as Pearson Prentice Hall. All rights reserved.

Poetry Collection: Eve Merriam, Emily Dickinson, Langston Hughes
Selection Test B

Critical Reading *Identify the letter of the choice that best completes the statement or answers the question.*

____ 1. Which statement best describes the two trees in "Simile: Willow and Ginkgo"?
A. The willow and the ginkgo are alike.
B. The willow is tougher than the ginkgo.
C. The willow is rough, while the ginkgo is delicate.
D. The willow is delicate, while the ginkgo is tough.

____ 2. What is the best context clue to the meaning of *crude* in this line from "Simile: Willow and Ginkgo"?

The ginkgo is like a <u>crude</u> sketch, / Hardly worthy to be signed.

A. The ginkgo
B. sketch
C. hardly worthy
D. to be signed

____ 3. Which of these lines from "Simile: Willow and Ginkgo" contains a simile?
A. "The willow is like an etching."
B. "The willow dips to the water."
C. "Thrust against the metal sky"
D. "*My eyes feast upon the willow.*"

____ 4. What is the meaning of *My eyes feast upon* in this line from "Simile: Willow and Ginkgo"?

<u>My eyes feast upon</u> the willow, / But my heart goes to the ginkgo.

A. I take delight in
B. I hold a banquet for
C. I roast
D. I eat too much of

____ 5. In "Simile: Willow and Ginkgo," the speaker's "heart goes to the ginkgo" because
A. the speaker thinks the ginkgo is more beautiful.
B. the speaker admires many of the ginkgo's qualities.
C. the speaker believes that the willow is too delicate.
D. the speaker has grown up among ginkgoes.

____ 6. What is the best meaning of "a wing" in the context of Emily Dickinson's poem?
Fame is a bee. / It has a song— / It has a sting— / Ah, too, it has <u>a wing</u>.

A. an ability to fly
B. part of a building
C. an arm
D. an air force unit

© Pearson Education, Inc., publishing as Pearson Prentice Hall. All rights reserved.

_____ 7. Which of these statements about "Fame Is a Bee" is correct?
A. Only the first line is a metaphor.
B. The whole poem is a metaphor.
C. The whole poem uses personification.
D. The last line is a simile.

_____ 8. The speaker of "Fame Is a Bee" sees fame as something that
A. everyone should seek.
B. nobody has control over.
C. everyone should try to avoid.
D. has both good and bad points.

_____ 9. In "April Rain Song," "Let the rain kiss you" is an example of
A. a simile using the word *like.*
B. a simile using the word *as.*
C. a metaphor.
D. personification.

_____ 10. What is the best context clue to the meaning of *still* in these lines from "April Rain Song"?

The rain makes <u>still</u> pools on the sidewalk.
The rain makes running pools in the gutter.

A. The rain makes
B. pools on the sidewalk
C. running pools
D. in the gutter

_____ 11. Which of these lines from "April Rain Song" contains personification?
A. "Let the rain sing you a lullaby."
B. "The rain makes still pools on the sidewalk."
C. "The rain makes running pools in the gutter."
D. "And I love the rain."

_____ 12. In "April Rain Song," the speaker's feelings about rain are
A. affectionate.
B. worried.
C. angry.
D. sad.

_____ 13. "Simile: Willow and Ginkgo," "Fame Is a Bee," and "April Rain Song" are alike in that they all
A. express an idea about life.
B. use rhyme and rhythm.
C. are sad and hopeless.
D. use figurative language.

© Pearson Education, Inc., publishing as Pearson Prentice Hall. All rights reserved.

Vocabulary and Grammar

____ 14. Which sentence uses the underlined vocabulary word *incorrectly*?
   A. We heard a <u>chorus</u> of howls from the coyotes on the hill.
   B. Anja is the only singer in the school <u>chorus</u>.
   C. A cactus <u>thrives</u> in a warm, dry climate.
   D. Our business <u>thrives</u> because we have many customers.

____ 15. The words *revise, recall,* and *respond* are alike in that they all
   A. have the same prefix.
   B. have the same meaning.
   C. have the same root.
   D. have the same suffix.

____ 16. When you *restate* a topic, you
   A. introduce it.
   B. add supporting details to it.
   C. say it again.
   D. make it more clear.

____ 17. Which of these sentences is imperative?
   A. My eyes feast upon the willow.
   B. What a beautiful song!
   C. Does fame have a sting?
   D. Let the rain kiss you.

Essay

18. Choose your favorite figure of speech in one of the poems in this collection—"Simile: Willow and Ginkgo," "Fame Is a Bee," or "April Rain Song." First, identify the figure of speech as a simile, a metaphor, or personification. Then, tell what is being compared and what the figurative language shows. Finally, tell what you like about the figure of speech.

19. The poets who wrote the poems in this collection—"Simile: Willow and Ginkgo," "Fame Is a Bee," and "April Rain Song"—were inspired by nature. Choose two of the poems. In an essay, explain how nature is involved in each one. Describe each poet's attitude toward nature as it is expressed in the poem, and point to at least two references to nature in each poem.

© Pearson Education, Inc., publishing as Pearson Prentice Hall. All rights reserved.

Vocabulary Warm-up Word Lists

Study these words from the poetry of Sandra Cisneros, Nikki Giovanni, and Theodore Roethke. Then, apply your knowledge to the activities that follow.

Word List A

accusers [uh KYOOZ erz] *n.* those who say that someone did something wrong
Brett's <u>accusers</u> said that he cheated on a test.

doorknob [DAWR nob] *n.* handle used to open a door
Latisha slowly turned the <u>doorknob</u> to open her front door

dough [DOH] *n.* bread, pie crust, or cookies before they are baked; a soft, thick, moist lump of flour and other ingredients
When my brother makes cookies, I love to eat the <u>dough</u> left at the bottom of the mixing bowl.

rushing [RUHSH ing] *v.* going somewhere quickly
Janet was <u>rushing</u> to school because she feared she would be late.

snores [SNAWRZ] *v.* breathes noisily through the mouth while sleeping
Carlos <u>snores</u> loudly in his sleep.

without [with OWT] *prep.* lacking or not having
Angela forgot her sneakers and went to gym class <u>without</u> them.

Word List B

crackling [KRAK ling] *adj.* making a lot of quick, sharp sounds
As Brian walked through the forest, he heard twigs <u>crackling</u> beneath his feet.

flashing [FLASH ing] *adj.* sparkling; sending out quick, stabbing beams of light
At the beach, I watched the sunlight <u>flashing</u> on the waves.

receive [ri SEEV] *v.* get or accept something
Marisol was happy to <u>receive</u> her first paycheck.

splinters [SPLIN tuhrz] *n.* thin, sharp pieces of wood
The old log broke into many <u>splinters</u>.

streaked [STREEKT] *adj.* having long, thin marks or stripes
Johnny's face was so <u>streaked</u> with dirt, he looked like a tiger.

underneath [uhn duhr NEETH] *prep.* under or below
Nadia's pencil had fallen <u>underneath</u> her desk.

© Pearson Education, Inc., publishing as Pearson Prentice Hall. All rights reserved.

Poetry Collection: Sandra Cisneros, Nikki Giovanni, and Theodore Roethke
Vocabulary Warm-up Exercises

Exercise A *Fill in each blank in the paragraph below with an appropriate word from Word List A. Use each word only once.*

Jodi loved to watch her family at breakfast time. This morning, her older sister was

[1] _____ out the door, while Jodi's two brothers were arguing. "Matt

kept me awake last night. He [2] _____ while he sleeps," her brother

Kevin complained. Jodi knew that this was true and said so.

   "Why are you two acting as my [3] _____ this morning?" Matt said.

   In the kitchen, Jodi's father was rolling out a batch of [4] _____ for

the pie he was making. She stopped to say hi to him before she took hold of the

[5] _____ and opened the door. Jodi knew her family was loud, but she

was happy to have them. She did not know what she would do [6] _____

her family!

Exercise B *Answer the questions with complete explanations.*

Example: Why do emergency vehicles such as police cars have <u>flashing</u> lights?
Flashing lights send out bursts of light. The lights get people's attention and let them know that the vehicle is coming.

1. If you lost a pencil <u>underneath</u> your desk, would you have to reach up or down to find it?
   _____

2. Would wet leaves make a <u>crackling</u> sound if you stepped on them? Why or why not?
   _____

3. If a stone is <u>streaked</u>, does that mean every part of it is the same color?
   _____

4. When you <u>receive</u> a gift, do you get to keep it? Why or why not?
   _____

5. Are <u>splinters</u> of wood generally big or small? Explain.
   _____

© Pearson Education, Inc., publishing as Pearson Prentice Hall. All rights reserved.

Poetry Collection: Sandra Cisneros, Nikki Giovanni, and Theodore Roethke

Reading Warm-up A

Read the following passage. Pay special attention to the underlined words. Then, read it again, and complete the activities. Use a separate sheet of paper for your written answers.

Maggie and Dan were in the kitchen mixing <u>dough</u> for a batch of cookies. They loved to watch the pale yellow paste turn into crisp, golden brown cookies as it baked. In the meantime, Grandpa had fallen asleep on the couch in the living room. His heavy breathing could be heard throughout the house.

"Listen to the way Grandpa <u>snores</u>," Maggie chuckled. "He makes a noise just like a truck when he sleeps!"

Dan gave his sister a mischievous smile. "Let's see if we can play a trick on him," he said.

Maggie slowly turned the <u>doorknob</u> to open the living room door. She and Dan silently crept into the room. Dan's eyes rested on the birdcage, with Grandpa's two prized parakeets. He went over to the birdcage and slowly reached inside. The bottom of the birdcage was covered in feathers.

Dan grabbed a feather and started to wave it in front of Grandpa's nose. The light, fluffy object tickled Grandpa and he snorted in his sleep. Maggie tried to get a feather too. Then all of a sudden, the parakeets woke up. They started to squawk loudly.

Grandpa woke with a start. Maggie and Dan looked at each other and started <u>rushing</u> out of the room. They knew they had been caught, and they could not leave quickly enough.

"Don't think you can leave this room so fast," Grandpa roared. "I know you were trying to play a trick on me. The birds saw you, and they are your <u>accusers</u>." Dan and Maggie looked at the parakeets, who seemed to know they were responsible for getting the two in trouble.

"You kids," Grandpa chuckled. "Don't think you can leave this room <u>without</u> getting a hug from me first!" He stood up and opened his arms. His grandchildren rushed into them. Grandpa smiled and wrapped his arms around Maggie and Dan.

1. Underline the words that tell what <u>dough</u> looks like. Then, name two things that are made by baking **dough**.

2. Underline the words that hint at the meaning of <u>snores</u>. Then, circle the description of how Grandpa sounds when he **snores**.

3. Circle the words that tell you what a <u>doorknob</u> is used for. Then, write a sentence using the word **doorknob**.

4. Underline the sentence that tells why Maggie and Dan were <u>rushing</u>. Then, use the word **rushing** in a sentence.

5. Underline the phrase that explains why the parakeets are called <u>accusers</u>. Describe **accusers** in your own words.

6. Circle the words that tell you what Grandpa wouldn't let the kids leave <u>without</u>. What is something that you would be unhappy **without**?

© Pearson Education, Inc., publishing as Pearson Prentice Hall. All rights reserved.

Name _____ Date _____

Poetry Collection: Sandra Cisneros, Nikki Giovanni, and Theodore Roethke
Reading Warm-up B

Read the following passage. Pay special attention to the underlined words. Then, read it again, and complete the activities. Use a separate sheet of paper for your written answers.

A greenhouse is a room made out of glass in which plants grow. Gardeners and farmers use greenhouses to grow plants year round. Many flowers that bloom only in the summer, for example, will bloom in the winter months in greenhouses.

The sight of sunlight <u>flashing</u> from the glass roof of a greenhouse can be dramatic. Reflecting light is not the main job of a greenhouse, though. A greenhouse works by trapping sunlight. The glass ceiling and walls let the sun's rays enter the room. The glass also holds in the heat created by the light of the sun. This warmth is trapped <u>underneath</u> the glass of the greenhouse. That means that plants can be grown in a stable and warm atmosphere.

Plants that are grown in a greenhouse need to <u>receive</u> proper care. The plants will thrive in the warm climate if they are tended by a gardener. He or she can control the greenhouse temperature so that each plant gets the right amount of heat to grow successfully.

If a gardener doesn't control the temperature properly, it can become too warm for the plants. If this happens, the leaves on the plants might wither, die, and drop off, littering the greenhouse floor. The sharp, quick, <u>crackling</u> sound dead leaves make when they are stepped on is hard to miss. Also, branches and tree trunks must be properly cared for in the greenhouse. If it gets too warm, the wood will dry out and can break into tiny, sharp <u>splinters</u>.

Today, many of the flowers and vegetables we buy are grown in greenhouses. Farmers like greenhouses because they create very attractive produce. The greenhouse's even and controlled environment means that fruits and vegetables are less likely to be <u>streaked</u> or spotted. Instead they usually have a rich, even color. They are also less likely to be infested by bugs.

1. Circle the words that explain what the greenhouse does to make <u>flashing</u> light. Then, explain why *flashing* sunlight might be dramatic or attention-getting.

2. Circle the words that explain what happens <u>underneath</u> the glass of a greenhouse. Then, use the word *underneath* in a sentence.

3. Underline the words that tell what the plants need to <u>receive</u> from a gardener. Then, tell what it means to *receive* something.

4. Circle the words that are clues to the meaning of the word <u>crackling</u>. What do you know that makes a *crackling* sound?

5. Underline the words that explain how <u>splinters</u> are created. What do *splinters* feel like when they get stuck in your skin?

6. Circle the phrase that means the opposite of <u>streaked</u>. Then, write a sentence with the word *streaked*.

© Pearson Education, Inc., publishing as Pearson Prentice Hall. All rights reserved.

Name _____ Date _____

Reading: Reread and Read Ahead to Find and Use Context Clues

Context is the situation in which a word or an expression is used. The words and phrases in the surrounding text give you clues to the meaning of the word. Sometimes a word has more than one meaning. You may recognize a word but not recognize the way in which it is used. **Reread and read ahead** to find and use context clues that clarify meanings of words with multiple meanings. Look at the following examples to see how context clarifies the meaning of *flow:*

> a river would stop / its <u>flow</u> if only / a stream were there / to receive it (*Flow* describes an action the river takes.)

> The streams <u>flow</u> into the river. (*Flow* is an action taken by the streams.)

As you read the poems, notice words that are used in unfamiliar or unusual ways. Use the context to help determine the meaning of the words.

DIRECTIONS: *Study the underlined word in each of the following lines from "Abuelito Who" or "Child on Top of a Greenhouse." Look for context clues in the lines that hint at the meaning of the word. On the line, write the context clues. Then, write two meanings for the word—first the meaning that fits the context, and then a meaning that does* not *fit the context. The first item has been done for you.*

1. "who is a <u>watch</u> and glass of water"

   Context clues: <u>"glass of water" (something put on a table next to a bed)</u>

   Meaning in context: <u>small device for telling time</u> **Second meaning:** <u>to look at</u>

2. "Who tells me in Spanish you are my <u>diamond</u> / who tells me in English you are my sky"

   Context clues: _____

   Meaning in context: _____ **Second meaning:** _____

3. "The wind billowing out the <u>seat</u> of my britches"

   Context clues: _____

   Meaning in context: _____ **Second meaning:** _____

4. "A <u>line</u> of elms plunging and tossing like horses"

   Context clues: _____

   Meaning in context: _____ **Second meaning:** _____

© Pearson Education, Inc., publishing as Pearson Prentice Hall. All rights reserved.

Poetry Collection: Sandra Cisneros, Nikki Giovanni, Theodore Roethke
Literary Analysis: Figurative Language

Figurative language is language that is not meant to be taken literally. Authors use figurative language to state ideas in fresh ways. They may use one or more of the following types of figurative language:

- **Similes** compare two different things using the word *like* or *as:* "who throws coins like rain"
- **Metaphors** compare two different things by stating that one thing is another: "who is dough and feathers"
- **Personification** compares an object or animal to a human by giving it human characteristics: "The half-grown chrysanthemums staring up like accusers"

A. DIRECTIONS: *Underline each example of figurative language. Above the underlined phrase, write S if it is a simile, M if it is a metaphor, and P if it is personification. The first use of figurative language has been identified as an example.*

        P

The <u>pitiless sun</u> beat down on us like hammers as we walked home. The books in our backpacks were as heavy as rocks. When we saw the fountain that welcomes visitors to the park, we raced toward it. Our feet pounded on the stones leading to the center of the fountain. We tore off our shoes and socks and splashed gratefully in the cool water. The fountain was an oasis in the desert on that hot day.

B. DIRECTIONS: *Complete the following chart. First, identify the type of figurative language in each item. Then, tell what the figurative language does. Finally, tell what it shows. Look back at the poem if you need more context.*

Figurative Language	Type	What It Does	What It Shows
1. who tells me in English you are my sky ("Abuelito Who")	metaphor	It compares the speaker to the sky.	It shows how much Abuelito loves the speaker.
2. an ocean would never laugh ("The World Is Not a Pleasant Place to Be")			
3. A line of elms plunging and tossing like horses ("Child on Top of a Greenhouse")			

© Pearson Education, Inc., publishing as Pearson Prentice Hall. All rights reserved.

Poetry Collection: Sandra Cisneros, Nikki Giovanni, Theodore Roethke
Vocabulary Builder

Word List

billowing   plunging

A. DIRECTIONS: *Read the incomplete paragraph below. On each line, write one of the words from the Word List. You will use each word twice. Think about the meaning of the word in the context of the paragraph.*

As we gathered around our bonfire on the beach, we were glad that we were not experiencing the [1] _____ temperatures that sometimes occur in late summer. A gust of wind carried [2] _____ smoke up toward the stars. Swimming in the ocean was far from our minds, but we could see a few surfers riding the [3] _____ waves in the distance. Our golden retriever, [4] _____ happily down one sand dune after another, would soon be ready for a rest.

B. DIRECTIONS: *Think about the meaning of the underlined word in each item below. Then, answer the question, and explain your answer.*

1. If you saw smoke <u>billowing</u> from the windows of a house, what would you do?

   _____

   _____

2. If you were in the market for a new computer and noticed <u>plunging</u> prices at an electronics store, would it be a good time to buy?

   _____

   _____

C. DIRECTIONS: *Write the letter of the group of words whose meaning is most nearly the same as that of the word from the Word List.*

____ 1. billowing
   A. blowing fiercely
   B. filling with air
   C. rocking gently
   D. sleeping soundly

____ 2. plunging
   A. unclogging something
   B. suddenly leaping over
   C. filling up with something
   D. suddenly dipping down

© Pearson Education, Inc., publishing as Pearson Prentice Hall. All rights reserved.

Poetry Collection: Sandra Cisneros, Nikki Giovanni, Theodore Roethke

Support for Writing a Poem with Figurative Language

Use this cluster diagram to gather ideas for a **poem** you will write using figurative language. First, write your subject in the oval at the center of the diagram. Then, in each circle around the oval, jot down one quality of your subject. Add more circles if you need them.

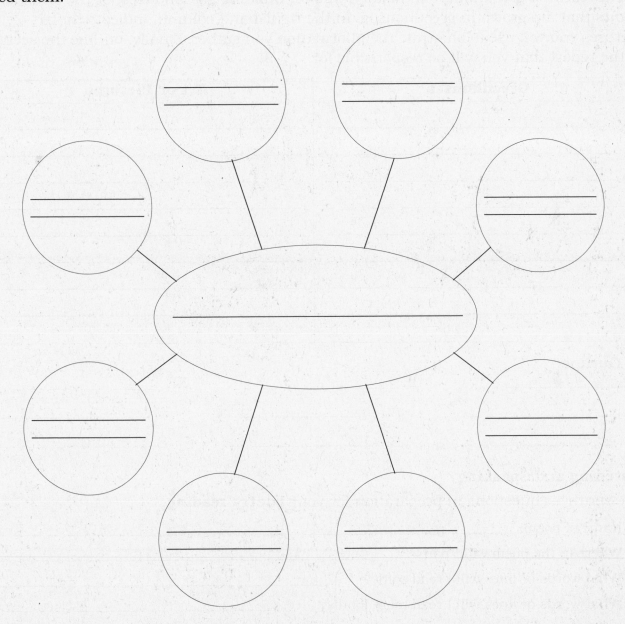

Now, use your notes to draft your poem. Be sure your poem has at least one simile, metaphor, or personification.

© Pearson Education, Inc., publishing as Pearson Prentice Hall. All rights reserved.

Poetry Collection: Sandra Cisneros, Nikki Giovanni, Theodore Roethke

Support for Extend Your Learning

Research and Technology

Use this chart as you work with a group of classmates to prepare a **multimedia report** on greenhouses. In the left-hand column, jot down information about greenhouses. You might research greenhouses in history, kits for building greenhouses, or the kinds of plants that are grown in greenhouses. In the right-hand column, indicate the art or pictures you will use to illustrate the information you gather. Finally, outline the section of the report that you will be responsible for.

Greenhouses	Art or Pictures
_____	_____
_____	_____
_____	_____
_____	_____
_____	_____
_____	_____
_____	_____

Outline:

I._____   II._____   III._____

A._____   A._____   A._____

B._____   B._____   B._____

Listening and Speaking

Answer these questions in preparation for your **poetry reading.**

Name of poem: _____

Where in the poem will I pause? _____

What words or lines will I read softly? _____

What words or lines will I read more loudly? _____

At what points in the poem will I show strong emotion? How should I read those parts?

_____

_____

Which words should I stress for effect? _____

_____

© Pearson Education, Inc., publishing as Pearson Prentice Hall. All rights reserved.

Name _____ Date _____

Enrichment: Elder Care

With people living longer, elderly people now form a large segment of our population. Many elderly people are completely independent and remain well physically and mentally into their nineties. Others need some degree of help doing such things as driving a car, shopping for groceries, paying bills, reading, walking, cooking, and doing home repairs. Many elderly people simply need company, especially if they do not have relatives living nearby or friends who visit regularly.

A. DIRECTIONS: *Some elderly people, like the grandfather in "Abuelito Who," live with members of their family. Answer these questions about situations in which elderly people live with their family.*

1. What might be one advantage to having an elderly relative live in the same house with his or her children, grandchildren, and/or great-grandchildren?

_____

_____

2. What might be one disadvantage of such a housing arrangement?

_____

_____

B. DIRECTIONS: *Helpers and caregivers provide a range of services to elderly people. Sometimes the helpers or caregivers are adults who make elder care their career. Sometimes they are students who work part-time after school or during the summer. List three skills or personal qualities that you think an elder-care helper should have.*

1. _____
2. _____
3. _____

C. DIRECTIONS: *Imagine that you are hiring a helper for an elderly relative. Write three questions that you would ask potential candidates. Then, exchange papers with a partner. Ask your partner the questions he or she wrote. Is your partner qualified for the job? Are you? Discuss why or why not.*

1. _____
2. _____
3. _____

© Pearson Education, Inc., publishing as Pearson Prentice Hall. All rights reserved.

Poetry Collections: Eve Merriam, Emily Dickinson, Langston Hughes;
Sandra Cisneros, Nikki Giovanni, Theodore Roethke

Build Language Skills: Vocabulary

Prefixes

When *re-* is added to the beginning of a word or a root, it adds the meaning "back" or "again." Look at the prefix *re-* in the word *restate*. *State* means "to express in words." *Restate* means "to express again in words." When you *restate* something, you say it again.

Word and Definition	Example
return: to go or give back	We *return* to school in the fall. Please *return* the book to the library.
renew: to make new again	The sun and rain will *renew* the wilted plant, making it thrive again.

A. DIRECTIONS: *Mentally add* re- *to each of the words in the box, thinking about the new word's meaning. Then, complete each sentence with one of the new words.*

placed	fuel	traced	unite

1. The historian _____ the steps of the explorers Lewis and Clark.
2. We were eager to _____ with our old friends.
3. Matt _____ the blown light bulb with a new one.
4. The plane landed at Kennedy Airport to _____ before continuing on.

Academic Vocabulary Practice

B. DIRECTIONS: *Revise each sentence so that the italicized Academic Vocabulary word is used logically. Be sure to keep the vocabulary word in your revision.*

1. After we saw the movie, we wanted to see a *preview* of it.

   _____

2. The teachers *restate* what they are planning to say.

   _____

3. I can *explain* anything I do not understand.

   _____

4. To figure out the meaning of a word from its *context*, look it up in a dictionary.

   _____

5. If you want to *define* a word, you should tell what language it comes from.

   _____

© Pearson Education, Inc., publishing as Pearson Prentice Hall. All rights reserved.

Poetry Collections: Eve Merriam, Emily Dickinson, Langston Hughes;
Sandra Cisneros, Nikki Giovanni, Theodore Roethke

Build Language Skills: Grammar

Sentence Functions

A **sentence** is a group of words that has a subject and a verb and expresses a complete thought. Sentences can be classified according to what they do—that is, according to their function or purpose. Notice that every sentence begins with a capital letter and ends with a punctuation mark. The kind of punctuation mark that is used depends on the function of the sentence.

Type	Function and End Punctuation	Example
Declarative	makes a statement; ends with a period	These poems are interesting.
Interrogative	asks a question; ends with a question mark	Which poem do you like best?
Imperative	gives an order or a direction; ends with a period or exclamation point	Let us read this poem. Please bring me that book. Catch it before it falls!
Exclamatory	expresses strong emotion; ends with an exclamation point	What a great poem to read aloud!

A. PRACTICE: *Classify these sentences according to their function. On the line following each sentence, write* declarative, interrogative, imperative, *or* exclamatory.

1. What a wonderful poem that is! _____
2. Elena, please read the first poem in this collection. _____
3. These poems are about nature, and those are about people. _____
4. Noah, give us your opinion. _____
5. Does anyone have anything to add? _____

B. Writing Application: *Write a brief paragraph about any of the poems in your textbook. In your paragraph, use at least one of each kind of sentence. Write a* D *above each declarative sentence,* Int *above each interrogative sentence,* Imp *above each imperative sentence, and* E *above each exclamatory sentence. Be sure to capitalize and punctuate each sentence correctly.*

_____

_____

_____

_____

_____

Unit 4 Resources: Poetry
© Pearson Education, Inc., publishing as Pearson Prentice Hall. All rights reserved.

Poetry Collection: Sandra Cisneros, Nikki Giovanni, Theodore Roethke

Selection Test A

Critical Reading *Identify the letter of the choice that best answers the question.*

____ 1. In "Abuelito Who," the pronoun *who* refers to Abuelito. Who is Abuelito?

A. a young child

B. the child's mother

C. the child's grandfather

D. the child's great-grandfather

____ 2. The speaker in "Abuelito Who" compares the way Abuelito throws coins to which of these?

A. a diamond

B. water

C. feathers

D. rain

____ 3. Which phrase from "Abuelito Who" contains a metaphor?

A. "whose little eyes are string"

B. "can't come out to play"

C. "sleeps in his little room"

D. "is hiding underneath the bed"

____ 4. The speaker in "Abuelito Who" says that Abuelito "used to laugh like the letter *k*." What does that mean?

A. His mouth looked like the letter *k* when he laughed.

B. His laugh sounded like the sound of the letter *k*.

C. He had a loud, cackling laugh that went on and on.

D. You could hardly hear him when he laughed.

____ 5. What type of figurative language is illustrated by this line from "The World Is Not a Pleasant Place to Be"?

an ocean would never laugh

A. a simile using the word *like*

B. a simile using the word *be*

C. a metaphor

D. personification

© Pearson Education, Inc., publishing as Pearson Prentice Hall. All rights reserved.

_____ 6. What makes life pleasant for the speaker in "The World Is Not a Pleasant Place to Be"?
   A. a good job
   B. nature
   C. being famous
   D. having a friend

_____ 7. In "The World Is Not a Pleasant Place to Be," *flow* means "running" or "moving." Which words in these lines are the best context clue to that meaning?

   a river would stop / its <u>flow</u> if only / a stream were there / to receive it

   A. a river would stop
   B. if only
   C. a stream were there
   D. to receive it

_____ 8. How does the speaker in "Child on Top of a Greenhouse" feel?
   A. excited
   B. scared
   C. dizzy
   D. guilty

_____ 9. In "Child on Top of a Greenhouse," which clue tells you that the day is windy?
   A. "My feet crackling splinters"
   B. "flashing with sunlight"
   C. "A few white clouds"
   D. "elms plunging and tossing"

_____ 10. In "Child on Top of a Greenhouse," why is "everyone pointing up and shouting"?
   A. They are surprised that the child is where he is.
   B. They see a helicopter coming to save the child.
   C. They know that a big storm is on its way.
   D. They are telling one another what happened.

_____ 11. What is one way in which "Abuelito Who" and "Child on Top of a Greenhouse" are alike?
   A. They are about naughty children.
   B. They are about love.
   C. They are about childhood memories.
   D. They are about sad feelings.

© Pearson Education, Inc., publishing as Pearson Prentice Hall. All rights reserved.

Vocabulary and Grammar

____ **12.** In which sentence is the underlined vocabulary word used *incorrectly*?
A. The jumper, <u>plunging</u> from the plane, waited before opening his parachute.
B. <u>Plunging</u> from the diving board, the diver hit the water without a splash.
C. It was a cold day, with smoke <u>billowing</u> from every chimney on the street.
D. Without any wind at all, the boat inched along, its sails <u>billowing</u>.

____ **13.** What is the meaning of the prefix *re-*?
A. back or again
B. here or there
C. before or after
D. to or across

____ **14.** When you *restate* a poem, what do you do?
A. You argue with what the poet has said.
B. You write a poem on the same subject.
C. You say the poem in your own words.
D. You memorize the whole poem.

____ **15.** Which of these sentences is interrogative?
A. Shut the door.
B. Everyone is pointing up!
C. The world is not a pleasant place to be.
D. Who is on top of the greenhouse?

Essay

16. Choose one of the poems in this collection—"Abuelito Who," "The World Is Not a Pleasant Place to Be," or "Child on Top of a Greenhouse." In an essay, explain the thoughts or feelings expressed by the speaker in that poem. Give one example from the poem to illustrate your point.

17. Which of the poems in this collection—"Abuelito Who," "The World Is Not a Pleasant Place to Be," or "Child on Top of a Greenhouse"—did you like best? In an essay, name your favorite, and tell why you liked it. For instance, did you agree with the ideas in the poem? Did the poem remind you of an experience you have had or one that you have heard or read about? Did you especially enjoy the language of the poem? Support your response by referring to a phrase or line that you especially liked.

© Pearson Education, Inc., publishing as Pearson Prentice Hall. All rights reserved.

Poetry Collection: Sandra Cisneros, Nikki Giovanni, Theodore Roethke
Selection Test B

Critical Reading *Identify the letter of the choice that best completes the statement or answers the question.*

_____ 1. "Abuelito Who" expresses a child's
   A. loving thoughts about a relative.
   B. sadness at a relative's death.
   C. lack of understanding about illness.
   D. nightmares about a ghost.

_____ 2. The pronoun *who* in the title of "Abuelito Who" refers to
   A. the speaker.
   B. the speaker's mother.
   C. the speaker's grandfather.
   D. the speaker's great-grandfather.

_____ 3. According to the speaker of "Abuelito Who," why does Abuelito not come downstairs today?
   A. He is too sick.
   B. He is too sad.
   C. He has died.
   D. He is sleeping.

_____ 4. Which phrase from "Abuelito Who" contains a metaphor?
   A. "Abuelito who throws coins like rain"
   B. "who is dough and feathers"
   C. "who used to laugh like the letter *k*"
   D. "who snores up and down"

_____ 5. In "Abuelito Who," the rain on the roof reminds the speaker of
   A. the coins Abuelito used to throw.
   B. the sound of Abuelito's laughter.
   C. the tears he or she has shed for Abuelito.
   D. the sound of Abuelito's shoes on the stairs.

_____ 6. In "The World Is Not a Pleasant Place to Be," "an ocean would never laugh" is an example of
   A. a simile using the word *like*.
   B. a simile using the word *as*.
   C. a metaphor.
   D. personification.

_____ 7. The speaker in "The World Is Not a Pleasant Place to Be" believes that what makes life worthwhile is
   A. having a good job and a loving family.
   B. being able to enjoy the beauty of nature.
   C. traveling to distant places.
   D. having someone to share life with.

© Pearson Education, Inc., publishing as Pearson Prentice Hall. All rights reserved.

_____ 8. How does the speaker in "Child on Top of a Greenhouse" feel?
   A. excited
   B. fearful
   C. dizzy
   D. naughty

_____ 9. What is the meaning of the figurative language in this line from "Child on Top of a Greenhouse"?

   The half-grown chrysanthemums staring up like accusers

   A. The flowers are like the child in that they are not fully grown.
   B. The child believes that the flowers are accusing him of something.
   C. The child knows that he will be punished for having done something wrong.
   D. The flowers look to the child like people accusing him of doing something wrong.

_____ 10. Which words in these lines from "Child on Top of a Greenhouse" provide the best context clue to the meaning of *line*?

   A few white clouds all rushing eastward,

   A *line* of elms plunging and tossing like horses

   A. A few white clouds
   B. all rushing eastward
   C. of elms
   D. like horses

_____ 11. In "Child on Top of a Greenhouse," why is "everyone pointing up and shouting"?
   A. They are surprised to see a child on top of a greenhouse.
   B. They are watching as the few white clouds rush eastward.
   C. They fear that the horses will trample the child.
   D. They are telling one another what has happened.

_____ 12. What is being compared in this simile from "Child on Top of a Greenhouse"?

   A line of elms plunging and tossing like horses

   A. trees and animals
   B. plunging and tossing
   C. a line and horses
   D. stillness and motion

_____ 13. "Abuelito Who" and "Child on Top of a Greenhouse" are alike in that they both
   A. are about children who have problems.
   B. are about children who are in trouble.
   C. recall childhood memories.
   D. describe happy and sad feelings.

_____ 14. In what way are "Abuelito Who" and "The World Is Not a Pleasant Place to Be" alike?
   A. Both are about respecting or loving all human beings.
   B. Both are about having someone care about you.
   C. Both are about depending on your family.
   D. Both are about someone teaching you values.

© Pearson Education, Inc., publishing as Pearson Prentice Hall. All rights reserved.

Vocabulary and Grammar

___ 15. Which sentence uses the underlined vocabulary word *incorrectly*?
A. <u>Plunging</u> down the trail in the dark, the horses missed the turnoff to the lodge.
B. <u>Plunging</u> into the cold water on the hot summer day, the swimmer felt refreshed.
C. It was a windy day, with clouds <u>billowing</u> and racing across the blue sky.
D. We watched as the <u>billowing</u> flags lay motionless on the hot, windless day.

___ 16. Based on what you know about the prefix *re-*, you can guess that *review* most likely means
A. to see through.
B. to see after.
C. to see before.
D. to see again.

___ 17. If you were to *define* a word, you would
A. make it clear.
B. state its meaning.
C. restate it.
D. preview it.

___ 18. Which of these sentences is imperative?
A. Shut the door, please.
B. An ocean would never laugh.
C. Who loves him?
D. Everyone was shouting.

Essay

19. Think about the poems you have read in this collection—"Abuelito Who," "The World Is Not a Pleasant Place to Be," and "Child on Top of a Greenhouse." Consider the speakers of two of those poems. In an essay, compare and contrast those speakers. Tell how they are alike and how they are different. Support your description with two details about each speaker.

20. What makes the world a pleasant place to be? Each of the speakers in the poems in this collection—"Abuelito Who," "The World Is Not a Pleasant Place to Be," and "Child on Top of a Greenhouse"—would have a different answer to that question. In an essay, tell how each speaker might answer it. Be sure to base your answer on information in each poem.

© Pearson Education, Inc., publishing as Pearson Prentice Hall. All rights reserved.

Vocabulary Warm-up Word Lists

Study these words from the poetry of Robert Frost and E.E. Cummings. Then, apply your knowledge to the activities that follow.

Word List A

keen [KEEN] *adj.* intense, lively, and alert
Laurie felt a <u>keen</u> sense of happiness after finishing first in the race.

mood [MOOD] *n.* an emotional state; the way someone feels
Victor was in a bad <u>mood</u> after he found out that he could not go on vacation.

rued [ROOD] *v.* felt regret or sorrow
Elise <u>rued</u> the fact that she had been careless and lost her wallet.

saved [SAYVD] *v.* rescued someone or something from danger
The firefighter <u>saved</u> the boy from the burning building.

shook [SHOOK] *v.* moved up and down or back and forth with quick, short movements
Mauricio <u>shook</u> the blanket to get out the wrinkles.

themselves [them SELVZ] *pro.* them and no one else; their own selves
People who look within <u>themselves</u> can learn a lot about who they are.

Word List B

always [AWL wayz] *adv.* happening often, continuously, or every time
Gina <u>always</u> enjoyed seeing her older brother and was never unhappy to go to his house.

balloon [buh LOON] *n.* an extremely large bag filled with a lighter-than-air gas and carrying a basket underneath that is used as a form of transportation
Jed dreamed about having a chance to ride in a hot-air <u>balloon</u>.

filled [FILD] *v.* to have made a container become full
Angie <u>filled</u> her glass with milk until some spilled over the top.

higher [HY er] *adv.* moving upward or above
Nate climbed <u>higher</u> up the mountain.

sailing [SAYL ing] *v.* traveling in a boat by means of large pieces of cloth that catch the wind
Every summer, Carmen went <u>sailing</u> on the lake.

visited [VIZ i ted] *v.* went to see people or places
Last year, Stephanie traveled to Washington, D.C., and <u>visited</u> all the important buildings in the city.

© Pearson Education, Inc., publishing as Pearson Prentice Hall. All rights reserved.

Name _____ Date _____

Poetry by Robert Frost and E.E. Cummings
Vocabulary Warm-up Exercises

Exercise A *Fill in each blank in the paragraph below with an appropriate word from Word List A. Use each word only once.*

Kelsey was in a very bad [1] _____ and had spent the day feeling sad.
She had accidentally broken her friend Julia's new skateboard. Julia was very angry.
Kelsey had been playing carelessly and she [2] _____ what she had
done. She felt a [3] _____ sense of regret but realized that feeling bad
would not change anything. Kelsey [4] _____ the skateboard and heard
the broken part rattling. Then, she took the skateboard to a repairman. He was able to
fix it, which made Kelsey very happy. She felt as if her friendship with Julia had been in
danger but the repairman had [5] _____ it. When Kelsey returned the
skateboard, she and Julia took turns riding on it. Now that the skateboard was fixed,
the two felt good about [6] _____ and their friendship as well.

Exercise B *Revise each sentence so that the underlined vocabulary word is used in a logical way. Be sure to keep the vocabulary word in your revision.*

Example: Marissa <u>visited</u> her grandfather and made sure never to see him.
Marissa <u>visited</u> her grandfather and got to see him every day.

1. Jose <u>filled</u> his backpack by taking all the books out of it.

   _____

2. As Evan walked down the staircase, he was moving <u>higher</u> in the building.

   _____

3. Melanie liked <u>sailing</u>, so she drove her car down the highway.

   _____

4. Because Luke <u>always</u> enjoyed reading, he made sure he never picked up a book.

   _____

5. The pilot inflated the hot-air <u>balloon</u> with dirt so that it could fly.

   _____

© Pearson Education, Inc., publishing as Pearson Prentice Hall. All rights reserved.

Poetry by Robert Frost and E.E. Cummings
Reading Warm-up A

Read the following passage. Pay special attention to the underlined words. Then, read it again, and complete the activities. Use a separate sheet of paper for your written answers.

What kind of <u>mood</u> are you in today? Are you happy or sad, excited or bored? A mood is the state of mind you are in at a specific moment in time. It can shape your outlook on life.

Some moods are happy ones. For example, if you have just won an award at school, you might feel a <u>keen</u> sense of accomplishment. You might feel intensely satisfied. This mood will stay with you as long as you feel this satisfaction. However, not all moods are good. If you did something you regret, that action might put you in a bad mood. You will have <u>rued</u> what you have done and feel unhappy about it.

Sometimes, the moods of the people around you can shape how you feel yourself. Think of a time when your friends have been unhappy. Have you been affected by their moods? Because moods travel between people, you may have felt sad while you were around them. However, if you were in a particularly good mood, you may have tried to make them feel better. Perhaps you <u>shook</u> their hands, patted their backs, and made a few jokes. You may have <u>saved</u> your friends from unwanted bad moods.

People who are in good moods often feel good about <u>themselves</u>. They feel that they are contented and happy people. This happiness can be catching. By being in a good mood, you make the people around you feel good about themselves. So the next time you feel happy or sad, think about the mood you are in. Think about how your mood affects the moods of those around you. Then, work to spread happiness by being in a good mood yourself!

1. Underline the words that tell what a <u>mood</u> is. What kind of *mood* do people enjoy most?

2. Circle the word in the next sentence that is a clue to the meaning of the word <u>keen</u>. Then, write a sentence using the word *keen*.

3. Circle the nearby word that has close to the same meaning as <u>rued</u>. Then, describe an action that you have *rued*.

4. Circle the words that tell what you perhaps <u>shook</u>. Use the word *shook* in a sentence of your own.

5. Underline the words that tell what you might have <u>saved</u> your friends from. Define *saved* as it is used in this passage.

6. Underline the phrase that tells you who feels good about <u>themselves</u>. How do you think most people feel about *themselves*?

© Pearson Education, Inc., publishing as Pearson Prentice Hall. All rights reserved.

Poetry by Robert Frost and E.E. Cummings
Reading Warm-up B

Read the following passage. Pay special attention to the underlined words. Then, read it again, and complete the activities. Use a separate sheet of paper for your written answers.

Have you ever seen a hot-air <u>balloon</u>? Hot-air balloons are large sacks made out of cloth that are pumped full of a gas that's lighter than air. The balloon rises when it is inflated with this gas. Many hot-air balloons have a basket underneath. People can stand in these baskets and be carried away by the balloon. This is a very exciting form of transportation. Traveling in a hot-air balloon feels like <u>sailing</u> through the air. The balloon catches the wind and moves through the air much like a ship moves across the sea.

A hot-air balloon flies by being <u>filled</u> with hot gas. The pilot pumps a gas like hydrogen or helium into the cloth bag of the balloon. These gasses are lighter than oxygen. The lighter gas causes the balloon to rise. The gas that fills a hot-air balloon must <u>always</u> be lighter than the air outside. If the gas is not lighter than the air at all times, the balloon will sink. It will be unable to fly.

The pilot controls a hot-air balloon carefully. He or she calculates the amount of air used to inflate it. When more helium or hydrogen is put into the balloon, it rises <u>higher</u>. The balloon moves upward into the sky. When a pilot wants the balloon to go downward, he or she releases some of the gas from the balloon into the air. This causes the balloon to sink toward the ground.

People have <u>visited</u> many beautiful locations in hot-air balloons. From these balloons, people can travel above the ground and see both new and familiar locations from a bird's-eye view. Maybe some day you will have the chance to travel in a hot-air balloon.

1. Underline the sentence that tells you what a hot-air <u>balloon</u> is. Would you like to ride in a *balloon*? Why or why not?

2. Circle the words that help describe what <u>sailing</u> is. Define *sailing* in your own words.

3. Circle the words that tell you what a hot-air balloon is <u>filled</u> with. Then, write a sentence using the word *filled*.

4. Underline the sentence that tells why the gas in a balloon <u>always</u> needs to be lighter than the air outside. What is something that a person might *always* need to do?

5. Underline the words that tell what a balloon does when it rises <u>higher</u>. Then, write a sentence using the word *higher*.

6. Circle the words that tell you what people have <u>visited</u> using hot-air balloons. Name a place *visited* by many people.

© Pearson Education, Inc., publishing as Pearson Prentice Hall. All rights reserved.

Poetry by Robert Frost and E.E. Cummings
Literary Analysis: Imagery

An **image** is a word or phrase that appeals to the five senses of sight, hearing, smell, taste, or touch. An image can also create a feeling of movement.

Writers use this sensory language—**imagery**—to create word pictures. The imagery in a word picture can appeal to more than one sense. For example, the images in the following lines appeal to the senses of both touch and taste:

Cold hands, warm mug;

sip of cocoa, mother's hug . . .

Imagery also helps a writer express mood. **Mood** is the feeling that a poem creates in a reader. A poem's mood might be fanciful, thoughtful, or lonely. In the lines above, the poet uses images that create a mood of cozy affection.

A. DIRECTIONS: *Listed below are images from Robert Frost's poem "Dust of Snow" and E.E. Cummings's poem "who knows if the moon's." For each image, list the senses that are involved. Choose from sight, hearing, smell, taste, touch. Also, explain whether the image creates a feeling of movement. Remember that each image can appeal to more than one sense.*

"Dust of Snow"	
Image	**Senses**
1. crow shaking branches of tree	
2. dust of snow falling on speaker	

"who knows if the moon's"	
Image	**Senses**
3. the moon as a balloon	
4. a balloon filled with pretty people	
5. going up above houses and steeples and cloud	
6. flowers picking themselves	

B. DIRECTIONS: *Tell what mood, or feeling, each poem's images help create.*

1. The mood of "Dust of Snow" is _____

2. The mood of "who knows if the moon's" is _____

© Pearson Education, Inc., publishing as Pearson Prentice Hall. All rights reserved.

Name _____ Date _____

Vocabulary Builder

Word List

> rued   steeples

A. DIRECTIONS: *Complete each sentence with a word from the Word List.*

1. Tall _____ can help travelers find a nearby village.
2. Sam _____ his poor brushing habits when the dentist found three cavities.

B. DIRECTIONS: *Revise each sentence so that the italicized vocabulary word is used correctly. Be sure to keep the vocabulary word in your revision.*

Original Sentence: When the soup grew cold, it began to *simmer*.

Revised Sentence: When the soup grew hot, it began to *simmer*.

1. When she saw the good grade on her paper, Kayla *rued* her preparation for the test.

_____

_____

2. It is difficult to see the churches' *steeples* from a distance.

_____

_____

C. DIRECTIONS: *On the line, write the letter of the word that is most nearly the same in meaning as the word in CAPITAL letters.*

____ 1. STEEPLES
   A. roads
   B. fences
   C. barrels
   D. towers

____ 2. RUED
   A. loved
   B. regretted
   C. viewed
   D. disturbed

© Pearson Education, Inc., publishing as Pearson Prentice Hall. All rights reserved.

Name _____ Date _____

Poetry by Robert Frost and E.E. Cummings
Support for Writing a Comparative Essay

Before you draft your essay comparing the role of nature in each poem, complete the graphic organizer below.

Nature	"Dust of Snow"	"who knows if the moon's"
Is nature seen as positive or negative?		
Does nature play a central role or a background role?		
Which words or phrases help create images of nature?	1. 2. 3. 4.	1. 2. 3. 4.

Now, use your notes to write an essay comparing the role nature plays in each poem. Be sure to include examples from the poems to support your ideas.

© Pearson Education, Inc., publishing as Pearson Prentice Hall. All rights reserved.

Name _____ Date _____

Poetry by Robert Frost and E.E. Cummings
Selection Test A

Critical Reading *Identify the letter of the choice that best answers the question.*

____ 1. Where does "Dust of Snow" take place?
A. in a barn
B. at the seashore
C. in a wooded area
D. on a city street

____ 2. In "Dust of Snow," the poet creates a word picture of nature. What is the main image in this word picture?
A. a branch
B. a crow
C. a heart
D. a walk

____ 3. In "Dust of Snow," the speaker says that something "Has given my heart / A change of mood." What has caused this change of mood?
A. seeing a crow perched in a tree
B. taking a walk in the woods
C. thinking about his day
D. having snow shaken on him

____ 4. In "Dust of Snow," what was going on *before* the speaker had a change of mood?
A. He was having a bad day.
B. He was in a hurry.
C. He was enjoying his day.
D. He felt that he was in danger.

____ 5. In "Dust of Snow," how does the speaker feel after his experience with nature?
A. happier
B. irritated
C. depressed
D. loving

____ 6. In "who knows if the moon's," the moon is the central image. To what sense does this image appeal?
A. hearing
B. smell
C. sight
D. touch

© Pearson Education, Inc., publishing as Pearson Prentice Hall. All rights reserved.

____ 7. In "who knows if the moon's," what is the moon seen as?
   A. a city
   B. a balloon
   C. a cloud
   D. a sailboat

____ 8. In "who knows if the moon's," the speaker imagines traveling somewhere. Where does he imagine traveling?
   A. to Earth from the moon
   B. to a nearby garden
   C. to the moon from Earth
   D. to a city in the sky

____ 9. Which phrase from "who knows if the moon's" creates a sense of movement?
   A. filled with pretty people
   B. houses and steeples and clouds
   C. go sailing away and away
   D. everyone's in love

____ 10. In "who knows if the moon's," how does the moon make the speaker feel?
   A. thoughtful
   B. lonely
   C. happy
   D. upset

____ 11. Which idea is conveyed in both "Dust of Snow" and "who knows if the moon's"?
   A. Nature can be playful.
   B. Nature can be harsh.
   C. Nature can be annoying.
   D. Nature can be mysterious.

____ 12. How might both speakers describe nature?
   A. challenging
   B. uplifting
   C. confusing
   D. gentle

© Pearson Education, Inc., publishing as Pearson Prentice Hall. All rights reserved.

___ 13. How is "who knows if the moon's" different from "Dust of Snow"?

    A. It has lines that rhyme.

    B. It tells about an actual event.

    C. It is about nature.

    D. It is a "what if" poem.

___ 14. To which sense do both "who knows if the moon's" and "Dust of Snow" appeal most strongly?

    A. hearing

    B. sight

    C. taste

    D. smell

Vocabulary

___ 15. In "who knows if the moon's," the speaker imagines "houses and *steeples* and clouds." What are *steeples*?

    A. rivers

    B. gateways

    C. crowds

    D. towers

Essay

16. In both "Dust of Snow" and "who knows if the moon's," the speaker has an experience with nature. In an essay, describe each speaker's experience. Then, describe a nature memory of your own. Which speaker's experience is most like yours? How? Use at least one example from one of the poems to support your answer.

17. Both Frost and Cummings use striking word pictures, or images, in their poems. Each word picture appeals to one or more of the senses—sight, hearing, smell, taste, or touch. In a brief essay, describe the main word picture in each poem by using at least one example from the poem. To what sense or senses does this image appeal?

© Pearson Education, Inc., publishing as Pearson Prentice Hall. All rights reserved.

Poetry by Robert Frost and E.E. Cummings
Selection Test B

Critical Reading *Identify the letter of the choice that best completes the statement or answers the question.*

_____ 1. Which sentence best summarizes the action in "Dust of Snow"?
  A. A crow in a tree shakes some snow onto the speaker.
  B. As the speaker walks through the snow, he sees a crow.
  C. A crow sits in a snowy hemlock tree on a winter day.
  D. The speaker sees a crow in a tree and thinks about his day.

_____ 2. In the first part of "Dust of Snow," the poet creates a word picture of nature. Which is *not* a part of that word picture?
  A. a crow in a tree
  B. a shaking branch
  C. falling snow
  D. the speaker's heart

_____ 3. "Dust of Snow" contains the image of a dusting of snow falling onto the speaker. To which senses does this image appeal?
  A. sound and smell
  B. sight and touch
  C. smell and touch
  D. sight and sound

_____ 4. Which mood do the images in "Dust of Snow" create?
  A. joyfulness
  B. irritation
  C. depression
  D. affection

_____ 5. Which statement would the speaker in "Dust of Snow" be most likely to make?
  A. Winter is the most glorious season of all.
  B. Crows are sometimes a nuisance.
  C. Nature has the power to lift one's spirits.
  D. People should try to hide their emotions.

_____ 6. In "who knows if the moon's," to where and with whom does the speaker imagine that "we" might travel?
  A. to Earth from the moon, with people from the moon
  B. to a nearby garden, with people from the city
  C. to the moon, with friends from Earth
  D. to a city in the sky, with people from that city

© Pearson Education, Inc., publishing as Pearson Prentice Hall. All rights reserved.

____ 7. Read this passage from "who knows if the moon's." To which two senses does it appeal?

> . . . why then / we'd go up higher . . . / than houses and steeples and clouds: / go sailing / away and away . . . .

   A. touch and sight
   B. hearing and movement
   C. touch and hearing
   D. movement and sight

____ 8. What is the speaker's desire in "who knows if the moon's"?
   A. to visit a nearby city
   B. to ride in a hot-air balloon
   C. to leave the everyday world
   D. to take a trip to outer space

____ 9. In "who knows if the moon's," the speaker imagines that in the place where he is going, it will always be spring. What does this suggest?
   A. that it is always fresh and exciting there
   B. that it is always one temperature there
   C. that it is pretty but unfriendly there
   D. that it is pretty but things never change there

____ 10. What mood is created by these lines from "who knows if the moon's"?

> . . . where / always / it's / Spring) and everyone's / in love and flowers pick themselves

   A. thoughtful
   B. lonely
   C. fanciful
   D. gloomy

____ 11. In literature, what is imagery?
   A. a feeling created by reading words in a poem
   B. a plot or use of language that is imaginary
   C. a word picture that appeals to the senses
   D. a word or phrase that calls forth a memory

____ 12. In both "Dust of Snow" and "who knows if the moon's," how does the speaker view nature?
   A. Nature is seen as being negative.
   B. Nature is seen as being positive.
   C. Nature is seen as being neutral.
   D. Nature is seen as being mysterious.

____ 13. With which statement would the speakers of both "Dust of Snow" and "who knows if the moon's" most likely agree?
   A. Nature can help us see life differently.
   B. The true meaning of nature is hard to discover.
   C. Nature challenges us to love others.
   D. Humans find nature only in distant places.

© Pearson Education, Inc., publishing as Pearson Prentice Hall. All rights reserved.

____ 14. An important image in "Dust of Snow" is the crow in the tree. Which image from "who knows if the moon's" appeals to the same sense?
A. sailing high in the sky
B. getting into a balloon
C. the moon in the night sky
D. the silence of night

____ 15. Which speaker says that he is changed by his encounter with nature?
A. the speaker of "Dust of Snow"
B. the speaker of "who knows if the moon's"
C. both speakers
D. neither speaker

Vocabulary

____ 16. When the speaker of "who knows if the moon's" imagines *steeples* down below, what is he imagining?
A. rivers in the countryside
B. gateways to villages
C. crowds in a city
D. towers on buildings

____ 17. When the speaker of "Dust of Snow" says that he *rued* a part of his day, what does he mean?
A. that he ruined a part of his day
B. that he forgot a part of his day
C. that he regretted a part of his day
D. that he recalled a part of his day

Essay

18. Both "Dust of Snow" and "who knows if the moon's" invite readers to see reality in new ways. In an essay, explain how each poem helped you see something in a way you had never seen it before. Clearly identify the person, object, or event from the poem that you see differently. Be specific about how the poet made this subject surprising.

19. Both "Dust of Snow" and "who knows if the moon's" contain striking images that appeal to a variety of senses. Imagine that you are either a painter, a dancer, or a musician. As this kind of artist, which poem interests you the most? Which image within that poem most strongly captures your attention? Why? Write an essay in response to these questions. Use at least two examples from the poem of your choice to support your response.

20. Both "Dust of Snow" and "who knows if the moon's" show human beings coming face to face with nature. In an essay, explain who meets nature in each poem, the part of nature they meet, and the effect or outcome of the encounter. With which speaker do you feel a greater connection? Why? Use at least two details from the poem of your choice to support your explanation.

© Pearson Education, Inc., publishing as Pearson Prentice Hall. All rights reserved.

Name _____ Date _____

Prewriting: Choosing Your Topic

Review the two writing prompts provided. Then, using the questions below, decide which topic you are better able to write.

Question	Description of Jobs of the Future	Persuasive Letter
How much do you know about this topic?		
How much does the topic interest you?		
What form does this topic require? (a summary, explanation, and so on)		
How comfortable are you with writing in this form?		

Drafting: Planning your Organization

Use the following graphic organizer to organize your writing. Include a thesis statement, a main idea for each paragraph, and the supporting details you will use to develop each paragraph

Thesis Statement:

Main idea/Subtopic:

Main idea/Subtopic:

Main idea/Subtopic:

Supporting Details:

Supporting Details:

Supporting Details:

© Pearson Education, Inc., publishing as Pearson Prentice Hall. All rights reserved.

Name _____ Date _____

Writing for Assessment: Integrating Grammar Skills

Revising for Strong, Functional Sentences

Make sure that each sentence in your writing serves the function it should, and that each one has the correct end punctuation.

The chart shows the four types of sentences and the specific punctuation mark for each.

Type of Sentence	Function	End Punctuation	Example(s)
declarative	makes a statement	period	Space travel is now available.
interrogative	ask a question	question mark	Would you go to Mars?
exclamatory	shows feelings	exclamation point	What a thrilling trip!
imperative	gives an order or a direction	period or exclamation point	Fasten your seat belt. Don't open that door!

Identifying Sentence Function and End Punctuation

A. DIRECTIONS: *On the first line, write the type of sentence. Then, on the other line, add the correct end punctuation.*

_____ 1. Please watch the program about Mars _____

_____ 2. Did you know Mars has four seasons _____

_____ 3. Mars is the fourth planet from the sun _____

_____ 4. I'll be on that spacecraft. It's a promise _____

Practice Using Sentence Function and End Punctuation

B. DIRECTIONS: *Rewrite each sentence using the type given in parentheses. Use the correct end punctuation.*

1. Recently methane gas has been detected on Mars. (question)

_____

2. Did you know that Mars is the planet most like Earth? (declarative)

_____

3. Did you know it is 47 million miles from Earth to Mars? (exclamatory)

_____

4. If you go to Mars, you must be prepared for lower gravity. (imperative)

_____

© Pearson Education, Inc., publishing as Pearson Prentice Hall. All rights reserved.

Unit 4: Poetry
Part 1 Benchmark Test 7

MULTIPLE CHOICE

Reading Skills *Read the selection. Then, answer the questions that follow.*

1   A saturated meadow,
2   Sun-shaped and jewel-small,
3   A circle scarcely wider
4   Than the trees around were tall;
5   Where winds were quite excluded,
6   And the air was stifling sweet
7   With the breath of many flowers,—
8   A temple of the heat.

9   There we bowed us in the burning,
10 As the sun's right worship is,
11 To pick where none could miss them
12 A thousand orchises;
13 For though the grass was scattered,
14 Yet every second spear
15 Seemed tipped with wings of color,
16 That tinged the atmosphere.

   —from "Rose Pogonias" by Robert Frost

1. Which of these makes most sense in the poem, if used in place of *excluded* in line 5?
   A. strong
   B. cold
   C. kept out
   D. not clear

2. Based on context clues in the poem, what kind of word is *stifling* in line 6?
   A. It names a type of flower.
   B. It describes air temperature.
   C. It names a certain taste.
   D. It describes a quality of fragrance.

3. Using context clues in the poem, what type of word is *orchises* in line 12?
   A. It refers to trees.
   B. It refers to meadows.
   C. It refers to insects.
   D. It refers to flowers.

4. Which of these, used in place of *tinged* in the last line of the poem, makes the most sense?
   A. spoiled
   B. colored
   C. softened
   D. brightened

© Pearson Education, Inc., publishing as Pearson Prentice Hall. All rights reserved.

Read the selection. Then answer the questions that follow.

1 The golden brooch my mother wore
2 She left behind for me to wear;
3 I have no thing I treasure more:
4 Yet, it is something I could spare.

5 Oh, if instead she'd left to me
6 The thing she took into the grave!-
7 That courage like a rock, which she
8 Has no more need of, and I have.

—from "The Courage That My Mother Had"
by Edna St. Vincent Millay

5. Which of these best helps you understand the meaning of *brooch* in line 1?
   A. golden, wore
   B. left, treasure
   C. mother, wear
   D. treasure, spare

6. What is the most likely meaning of *spare* in line 4 of the poem?
   A. show mercy to
   B. give up
   C. have left over
   D. somewhat thin

7. Which meaning of *grave* in line 6 is most likely, based on context clues in the poem?
   A. deserving of serious thought
   B. a place where someone is buried
   C. to carve or cut
   D. having a serious look

Read the selection. Then answer the questions that follow.

Instructions for Changing Ink Cartridges in Your Printer
   1. Press and hold the *On* button for 2 seconds. A green light will flash.
   2. Lift the entire scanner unit.
   3. Remove the old cartridge and dispose of it properly.
   4. Remove the new cartridge from its package.
   5. Lower the cartridge into its holder.

8. Which of these can best help you clarify technical language in an instruction manual?
   A. knowing the author's purpose
   B. skimming the text
   C. looking at the surrounding text
   D. drawing a diagram

© Pearson Education, Inc., publishing as Pearson Prentice Hall. All rights reserved.

9. Of these, which might best help you understand the meaning of *scanner unit* in the selection?
   - A. rereading the selection
   - B. checking the company Web site
   - C. consulting a technical dictionary
   - D. studying a diagram of the printer parts

10. Based on context clues in the selection, what is the likely meaning of *cartridge*?
    - A. a type of container
    - B. a type of paper
    - C. a type of ink
    - D. a type of printer

Literary Analysis

11. Which of these best defines *rhythm* in poetry?
    - A. the repetition of sounds at the ends of words
    - B. the sound pattern created by stressed and unstressed syllables
    - C. a regular pattern of rhyming words in a poem
    - D. a repeated line or group of lines in a poem

12. How many stressed syllables are in the following lines of poetry?

    The spider's a curious creature / She has a remarkable feature.

    - A. 4
    - B. 6
    - C. 8
    - D. 10

13. What is an example of two rhyming words in the following lines of poetry?

    Softly, as if instinct with thought,
    They float and drift, delay and turn;
    And one avoids and one is caught,
    Between an oak-leaf and a fern.

    —from "Silkweed" by Philip Henry Savage

    - A. if, with
    - B. drift, delay
    - C. thought, caught
    - D. one, fern

14. Which of these is a type of figurative language?
    - A. metaphor
    - B. rhythm
    - C. definition
    - D. dialogue

© Pearson Education, Inc., publishing as Pearson Prentice Hall. All rights reserved.

15. Which line of poetry contains an example of a simile?
    A. The silkweed goes a-gypsying.
    B. She walks the sodden pasture lane,
    C. Drops floated on the pool like pearls,
    D. Moonlight spilled on the meadow,

16. Which of these is an example of the use of personification?
    A. As fleet as a gazelle, she ran across the meadow toward home.
    B. The car's engine coughed, sputtered, and died.
    C. His harsh words hung in the air like a dark cloud.
    D. The pond at twilight contained a symphony of sounds.

17. Which of these best defines imagery in literary works?
    A. the use of imagination in writing
    B. comparing two unlike things
    C. language that appeals to the senses
    D. feelings that language produces

18. Which sense do the following lines of poetry appeal to?

    We ran as if to meet the moon / That slowly dawned behind the trees,

    A. hearing
    B. touch
    C. smell
    D. sight

19. Which of these best describes the mood created by the following lines of poetry?

    The desolate, deserted trees, / The faded earth, the heavy sky,

    A. peaceful
    B. lonely
    C. happy
    D. thoughtful

Vocabulary: Prefixes

20. What is the meaning of *prevent* in the following sentence?

    Stretching before and after exercise will help prevent injuries.

    A. keep from happening
    B. make worse
    C. greatly improve
    D. return to health

Unit 4 Resources: Poetry
© Pearson Education, Inc., publishing as Pearson Prentice Hall. All rights reserved.

21. Which definition best fits the word *prehistoric* in the following sentence?

We learn about prehistoric animals such as dinosaurs from fossils and bones.

   A. no longer living
   B. before written history
   C. very large
   D. throughout history

22. What is the meaning of *refund* in the following sentence?

The producers will refund our money because the concert was canceled.

   A. add to
   B. take away
   C. give back
   D. save for later

23. Which definition best fits the word *precede* in the following sentence?

A light dinner will precede tonight's program.

   A. follow
   B. come before
   C. take place
   D. accompany

24. What is the meaning of *revive* in the following sentence?

Can we ever revive the lost art of letter writing?

   A. make corrections
   B. decide on
   C. put in good condition
   D. bring back into use

Grammar: Sentences

25. What is the simple subject of the following sentence?

Blueberries are healthful and delicious.

   A. blueberries
   B. are
   C. healthful
   D. delicious

26. What is the compound subject of the following sentence?

Ramon and Celia are two students who excel in math and science.

   A. Ramon and Celia
   B. two students
   C. who excel
   D. math and science

Unit 4 Resources: Poetry
© Pearson Education, Inc., publishing as Pearson Prentice Hall. All rights reserved.

27. Which sentence contains a compound subject?
    A. Two small lizards crawled up the wall.
    B. Dolphins and porpoises look similar.
    C. I picked fresh strawberries and grapes.
    D. Yvonne turned and gave a yelp.

28. Which of these best describes the following sentence?

    Give your ticket to the man in the red jacket.

    A. declarative
    B. interrogative
    C. imperative
    D. exclamatory

29. Which of these is an interrogative sentence?
    A. Will you attend the free concert?
    B. Shelby rescued a frog from the pool.
    C. Watch out for the deep hole!
    D. Read every question carefully.

30. Which sentence uses correct punctuation?
    A. Did Amy find her lost bracelet.
    B. Don't leave your bike in the rain?
    C. Where will the meeting take place.
    D. The view from here is fantastic!

31. Which of these best describes the function of the following sentence?

    Some people prefer to go to bed early and wake up early.

    A. asks a question
    B. shows strong feelings
    C. makes a statement
    D. gives an order

ESSAY

Writing

32. Think of a book, story, or poem you have enjoyed recently. Write a beginning sentence for a letter to the author. In the sentence, mention the name of the work and state your reaction to it.

33. Imagine that you will write a poem about the weather. Make a cluster diagram that shows the weather qualities that you want to include. Include at least one example of figurative language in your diagram, such as "lightning dancing down from the clouds."

34. Imagine that you are writing for assessment and have expressed the following main idea in response to a writing prompt. List three details that you might use to support this opinion.

    I think that the extra money our school raised should be used to provide more field trips.

© Pearson Education, Inc., publishing as Pearson Prentice Hall. All rights reserved.

Unit 4: Poetry
Part 2 Concept Map

Reading Skills and Strategies:
Paraphrasing

Academic Vocabulary words you can use to discuss making predictions

you can **paraphrase**

by

rereading any difficult lines

and by

rereading **aloud fluently according to punctuation**

(demonstrated in this selection)

Selection name:

Literary Analysis:
Poetry

Poetry

has

different **forms**

and

sound devices

(demonstrated in this selection)

Selection name:

(demonstrated in this selection)

Selection name:

Basic Elements of Poetry
- Sound Devices
- Figurative Language
- Sensory Language

Forms of Poetry
- Narrative
- Lyric
- Concrete
- Haiku
- Limerick

Comparing Literary Works:
Sensory Language

is used

to stir up memories and associations

to create images or word pictures

(demonstrated in these selections)

Selection names:

1.

2.

Reading Informational Materials:
Applications

You can **read to perform a task**

by

previewing, paraphrasing, and reviewing

(demonstrated in this selection)

Selection name:

Part 2 Student Log

Complete this chart to track your assignments.

Writing	Extend Your Learning	Writing Workshop	Other Assignments

© Pearson Education, Inc., publishing as Pearson Prentice Hall. All rights reserved.

Unit 4: Poetry
Part 2 Diagnostic Test 8

MULTIPLE CHOICE

Read the selection. Then, answer the questions that follow.

Of all the Greek gods and goddesses, Hades was the least liked. He was a grim fellow compared to his brothers Zeus and Poseidon. He possessed all the non-living things of the earth—the gems and metals—but not the life giving soil or the autumn harvests. Hades ruled a barren world without color or sunshine, known as the Underworld, or Land of the Dead.

According to the early Greeks, when people died, they would descend into the Land of Hades. The ferryman Charon would then row them across the River Styx. On the other side of this river, they met the three-headed dog Cerberus who guarded the gates into the Underworld.

The early Greeks believed everyone went to the land of Hades after they died. If they had lived a good life, however, their time in the Underworld was not too bad.

Later, Romans adopted the Greek gods and changed their names. *Zeus* became *Jupiter, Poseidon* became *Neptune,* and *Hades* became *Pluto.*

Today people no longer believe in the Greek and Roman gods. Nevertheless, the name *Hades,* or *Pluto,* is still with us. For example, the rare metal plutonium is named after him as is the name of the ninth and darkest planet in our universe.

1. What kind of creature was Hades?
   A. a god
   B. a three-headed dog
   C. a ferryman
   D. an early Greek

2. What did Hades rule?
   A. the River Styx
   B. the Underworld
   C. Greece
   D. the harvests

3. Why was Hades not liked?
   A. He had the job of guiding people to the underworld.
   B. He was the most powerful of the gods.
   C. He was grim and lived in a dreary place.
   D. He was a frightening figure.

4. According to the Greeks, what happened when people died?
   A. They lived on the River Styx.
   B. They joined the world's non-living things.
   C. They went to be with the gods.
   D. They had to spend time in the Under-world.

5. Who was the ferryman of the Underworld?
   A. Charon
   B. Cerberus
   C. Neptune
   D. Zeus

6. What prevented the living from passing into the Underworld?
   A. Hades stopped them from entering.
   B. Poseidon forbade them from entering.
   C. The gates were guarded by Cerberus.
   D. They could not cross the River Styx.

© Pearson Education, Inc., publishing as Pearson Prentice Hall. All rights reserved.

7. How are the Greek and Roman gods different?
   A. The Romans did not worship gods.
   B. The names of the gods are different.
   C. Roman gods were more powerful.
   D. The Greeks had many more gods.

8. Which planet is named for the god of the Underworld?
   A. Mars
   B. Jupiter
   C. Charon
   D. Pluto

Read the selection. Then, answer the questions that follow.

Gambia is a small country located on the west coast of Africa. Its capital city is Banjul. Gambia's main resource comes from its proximity to the Gambia River, which is a major African water route. Peanuts, an important crop to Gambia's economy, are exported to many countries.

Many kinds of trees grow in Gambia, including cedar, mahogany, and mangrove. Gambia is also home to many kinds of animals, such as the leopard, wild boar, antelope, hippopotamus, and crocodile. In the past, Gambia's wild animals were abundant; today, however, their numbers have decreased as the country's forests have been cleared for farming.

The largest of Gambia's many ethnic groups is the Mandinka people. Although English is the official language of Gambia, the different groups speak their own languages. Gambians follow the customs or beliefs of a number of religions, however most are Muslim. Some practice Christianity or traditional religions.

Gambia's most important neighbor is Senegal. Gambia and Senegal have a treaty that states that the two countries agree to work together to improve their countries' economies.

The flag of Gambia, adopted in 1965, has three horizontal stripes of red, blue, and green. The colors are symbolic: red stands for the sun, blue stands for the Gambia River, green stands for the land.

9. In what part of the world is Gambia located?
   A. in the East Indies
   B. on the continent of Africa
   C. on the continent of South America
   D. in the Southern Hemisphere

10. What is the most important part of Gambia's economy?
    A. peanuts
    B. trees
    C. the animals
    D. the Gambia River

11. What types of animals live in Gambia?
    A. cattle
    B. wild animals
    C. farm animals
    D. zoo animals

12. Why have the numbers of Gambia's wild animals decreased?
    A. Their land has been turned into farms.
    B. Many have migrated to other areas.
    C. Large numbers were killed by hunters.
    D. Many have been sent to zoos.

13. What kinds of people live in Gambia?
    A. only Christians
    B. only the Mandinka people
    C. many different ethnic groups
    D. only English-speaking people

© Pearson Education, Inc., publishing as Pearson Prentice Hall. All rights reserved.

14. Why has Gambia signed a treaty with Senegal?

    A. People from Gambia travel to Senegal.   **C.** Gambia wants to join with Senegal.

    B. Senegal and Gambia were old enemies.   **D.** Senegal is an important neighbor.

15. What do the colors of Gambia's flag symbolize?

    A. the animals, the river, and the food   **C.** the sun, the land, and the Gambia River

    B. the sun, the river, and the crops   **D.** the sun, the forests, and the farms

Vocabulary Warm-up Word Lists

Study these words from the poems. Then, apply your knowledge to the activities that follow.

Word List A

caught [KAWT] *v.* stuck, trapped, or captured
When my coat got <u>caught</u> in the door, the door would not close properly.

flee [FLEE] *v.* run away; escape
The cat tried to <u>flee</u> when it saw the dog.

sailor [SAY luhr] *n.* person who guides a boat or works on a boat
Jared wanted to be a <u>sailor</u> because he loved to be on the sea.

sea [SEE] *n.* ocean
I won't go swimming in the <u>sea</u>; the waves are too big and the water is too cold.

skimming [SKIM ing] *adj.* gliding; moving swiftly and lightly over a surface
With my new skates, I was <u>skimming</u> smoothly around the rink.

splash [SPLASH] *n.* the sound made when a person or an object hits water
I heard the <u>splash</u> when Jessica jumped into the pool.

Word List B

asphalt [AS fawlt] *adj.* made of the black cementlike substance used for the surface of playgrounds and roads
We play football on grass rather than <u>asphalt</u> pavement so we don't get hurt.

flaw [FLAW] *n.* break; crack
If they don't fix that <u>flaw</u> in the wall, it might fall down.

silence [SY luhns] *n.* complete quiet
At night, there is <u>silence</u> in my house; there isn't a single sound.

sway [SWAY] *v.* move back and forth
Look at those trees <u>sway</u> in the strong wind.

swerve [SWERV] *v.* turn sharply and suddenly
Mom had to <u>swerve</u> so she didn't hit the pig that ran into the road.

whirring [WER ing] *adj.* making a whizzing or buzzing sound
I hate the <u>whirring</u> sound that the wind-up toy makes.

© Pearson Education, Inc., publishing as Pearson Prentice Hall. All rights reserved.

Poetry Collection: Bashō, Anonymous, and Lillian Morrison
Vocabulary Warm-up Exercises

Exercise A *Fill in each blank in the paragraph below with an appropriate word from Word List A. Use each word only once.*

Claire loved the cartoon about Sammy the [1] _____. In it, Sammy sails his boat out onto the [2] _____. All of a sudden, he hears a huge [3] _____. It is the sound of a giant whale dropping its tail into the water. Sammy tries to [4] _____ from the whale. For a while, he is able. He keeps his boat [5] _____ smoothly across the water, a few feet in front of the whale's open mouth. After a mile or two, the whale catches up. Sammy escapes, however, when the boat gets [6] _____ in the whale's mouth. Sammy jumps into the water and swims back to the beach.

Exercise B *Revise each sentence so that the underlined vocabulary word is used in a logical way. Be sure to keep the vocabulary word in your revision.*

Example: That's too <u>expensive</u>; pick out something that costs more.
That's too <u>expensive</u>; pick out something that costs less.

1. Buy the mirror with a <u>flaw</u> in it to make sure you can see yourself clearly.

   _____

2. The <u>asphalt</u> pavement was soft as a pillow.

   _____

3. Stop yelling and screaming; I can't stand the <u>silence</u>.

   _____

4. We built a strong, solid building out of bricks to make sure it would <u>sway</u> in the breeze.

   _____

5. My bike began to <u>swerve</u> on the dry part of the road.

   _____

6. I hate noise when I am studying, so I study next to that <u>whirring</u> clock.

   _____

© Pearson Education, Inc., publishing as Pearson Prentice Hall. All rights reserved.

Poetry Collection: Bashō, Anonymous, and Lillian Morrison
Reading Warm-up A

Read the following passage. Pay special attention to the underlined words. Then, read it again, and complete the activities. Use a separate sheet of paper for your written answers.

George had always loved the North Carolina shore. Whenever his family took a vacation, he spent hours staring at the <u>sea</u>; there was just something special about the ocean. The only thing that ever bothered him was his younger brother, Sam. Sometimes Sam was so whiny it made him furious. One day, Sam was doing some nonstop whining and George decided that he had to <u>flee</u>. To escape from his brother, he walked across the road to the bay side of the island.

George looked out into the water. For the first time, he noticed the sailboats. There must have been dozens of them, <u>skimming</u> easily across the water. He was amazed at how they seemed to be gliding, their movements so swift and smooth. They almost looked like they were dancing. He watched them for what seemed like hours. He felt like he was in a dream.

A nearby <u>splash</u> woke him out of his dreaming. It was a girl, about his age, throwing a fishing line into the bay.

"Looking at the boats?" asked the girl. "I love boats. I'm going to be a <u>sailor</u> when I get older and get a job working on a fishing boat."

"These sailboats are amazing," replied George. "I could watch them for hours. In fact, I think I have been watching them for hours."

Suddenly the girl pulled on her fishing line with a hard tug.

"Do you have a fish?" asked George.

"No," she replied while walking into the water. "I think the hook is <u>caught</u> on a rock or something."

"Nice talking with you," said George. "I've got to get back to my family."

"Come back sometime and we can fish together," the girl said.

George did, many times during his vacation.

1. Underline the nearby word that has the same meaning as <u>sea</u>. Then, write a sentence using the word *sea*.

2. Circle the words that tell what George needed to <u>flee</u> from. Then, tell what *flee* means.

3. Circle the nearby word that has nearly the same meaning as <u>skimming</u>. Then, write a sentence describing something else you might see *skimming*.

4. Circle the words that tell what made the <u>splash</u>. Then, tell what *splash* means.

5. Underline the words that tell one place a <u>sailor</u> might work. Then, describe another place a *sailor* might work.

6. Underline the word that tells what the hook might be <u>caught</u> on. Then, tell what *caught* means.

© Pearson Education, Inc., publishing as Pearson Prentice Hall. All rights reserved.

Poetry Collection: Bashō, Anonymous, and Lillian Morrison
Reading Warm-up B

Read the following passage. Pay special attention to the underlined words. Then, read it again, and complete the activities. Use a separate sheet of paper for your written answers.

When you are searching for a big thrill, there is no better place to look than a roller coaster. These amusement park rides are one of the best ways to scare yourself silly while staying safe.

To the roller coaster fan, there is nothing like the start of the ride. The cars head up the first hill. Riders stare down at the <u>asphalt</u> parking lots as the coaster climbs higher and higher. Then, the cars reach the top. There is a brief moment of near <u>silence</u>; the riders are afraid to make a sound. The only noise is made by the <u>whirring</u> wheels on the track.

Then the quiet is broken the moment the cars start roaring downhill. The riders scream and yell in a mixture of joy, excitement, and fear. The ride has really begun.

Today, roller coasters are scarier then ever because of inventive new designs. The cars <u>swerve</u> suddenly to the side. They even turn riders completely upside down.

Modern roller coasters are made out of steel. In years past, however, roller coasters were made out of wood. There are still some wooden coasters creaking along in parks around the country. For some reason, they seem even scarier than the faster, newer steel ones. Maybe it is because the cars seem to <u>sway</u> more as they rocket down a wooden track. Maybe it is because they look as if they would fall apart when a strong wind blows.

No matter what they look like, roller coasters are usually very safe. The people who build them design them with safety in mind. In addition, inspectors check roller coasters regularly to make sure there is not a single <u>flaw</u> on the track. It is important, however, for riders to always obey the rules of a ride.

1. Underline the words that tell what area is <u>asphalt</u>. Then, describe another place that could be *asphalt*.

2. Circle the words that tell where you will find near <u>silence</u> on a roller-coaster ride. Then, describe another place you might find near *silence*.

3. Circle the words that tell what is <u>whirring</u>. Then, tell what else might make a *whirring* sound.

4. Underline the words that tell where the cars go when they <u>swerve</u>. Then, tell what *swerve* means.

5. Underline the words that tell when the cars seem to <u>sway</u> more. Then, tell what *sway* means.

6. Underline the words that tell where inspectors are checking for a <u>flaw</u>. Then, tell what *flaw* means.

© Pearson Education, Inc., publishing as Pearson Prentice Hall. All rights reserved.

Poetry Collection: Bashō, Anonymous, Lillian Morrison
Reading: Reread to Paraphrase

Paraphrasing is restating an author's words in your own words. Paraphrasing difficult or confusing passages in a poem helps you clarify the meaning. Use these steps to help you:

- First, stop and reread any difficult lines or passages.
- Next, identify unfamiliar words. Find their meaning and replace them with words that mean the same or nearly the same thing.
- Then, restate the lines in your own words, using everyday speech.
- Finally, reread the lines to see if your paraphrase makes sense in the poem.

A chart such as the one below can be useful in helping you paraphrase.

DIRECTIONS: *In the left column of the chart are passages from the poems in this collection. Underline unfamiliar words. Find the meanings of these words and write the meaning in the second column. In the third column, paraphrase the passage. The first one has been done for you as an example.*

Passage	New Words	Paraphrase
Example: Skimming an asphalt sea	skimming: moving swiftly; asphalt: pavement	gliding swiftly over the sidewalk
1. I swerve, I curve, I sway;		
2. An old silent pond . . .		
3. A flea and a fly in a flue Were caught,		
4. a flaw in the flue		

© Pearson Education, Inc., publishing as Pearson Prentice Hall. All rights reserved.

Poetry Collection: Bashō, Anonymous, Lillian Morrison
Literary Analysis: Forms of Poetry

Poets use different **forms of poetry** suited to the ideas, images, and feelings they want to express. The following are three poetic forms:

- A **haiku** is a Japanese verse form with three lines. Line 1 has five syllables, line 2 has seven syllables, and line 3 has five syllables. Haiku often focuses on nature. It tries to capture a moment by giving you a few quick images or word-pictures that help you see and hear something in a new way.
- A **limerick** is a short, funny poem of five lines. The first, second, and fifth lines rhyme and have three beats, or stressed syllables. The third and fourth lines rhyme and have two strong beats.
- A **concrete poem** has words arranged in a shape that reflects the subject of the poem.

DIRECTIONS: *Answer the questions about each form of poetry below.*

1. "Haiku" by Bashō

	What do you see?	**What do you hear?**
An old silent pond . . .		
A frog jumps into the pond,		
splash! Silence again.		

2. "Limerick" by Anonymous

Underline each *stressed* syllable in each line. Then, identify the rhyme scheme or pattern by writing the letters *a* or *b* at the end of each line. Give each rhyme a different letter. For example, write the letter *a* at the end of the first line and *a* at the end of each line that rhymes with line one.

A flea and a fly in a flue _____
Were caught, so what could they do? _____
  Said the fly, "Let us flee." _____
  "Let us fly," said the flea. _____
So they flew through a flaw in the flue. _____

3. "The Sidewalk Racer" by Lillian Morrison

Concrete means "something real, something that can be touched," such as an apple, a tree, or a cell phone. List three subjects that you think might be good choices for a concrete poem.

_____

_____

_____

© Pearson Education, Inc., publishing as Pearson Prentice Hall. All rights reserved.

Name _____ Date _____

Vocabulary Builder

Word List

flee   flaw   skimming

A. DIRECTIONS: *In the limerick below, fill in each blank with the correct vocabulary word.*

A crow on a flue belching smoke

Said, "Something's amiss, that's no joke.

What a _____ in the day,

I'll go _____ away

If I don't _____ this flue, I will choke."

B. DIRECTIONS: *A word map can help you explore the meaning of a word. Make a word map for each vocabulary word. The first one has been started for you.*

1.

Definition: error that spoils something	**FLAW**	**Synonym:**

Sentence: Laziness is a flaw in his usual good character.

2.

Definition:	**FLEE**	**Synonym:**

Sentence:

3.

Definition:	**SKIMMING**	**Synonym:**

Sentence:

© Pearson Education, Inc., publishing as Pearson Prentice Hall. All rights reserved.

Poetry Collection: Bashō, Anonymous, Lillian Morrison
Support for Writing a Poem

You have read examples of a haiku, a limerick, and a concrete poem. Now, try writing a poem of your own, using one of these forms.

What form of poetry will you use? _____

What do you need to remember about this form? Take notes here.

_____

_____

_____

_____

_____

Use the lines below to jot down ideas for your poem. If you're writing a haiku, you will want to think about nature images. If you're writing a limerick, think up a silly character or start with place names that sound funny and will be easy to rhyme—for example, "Chicago." If you're writing a concrete poem, think of a real subject that suggests a shape—for example, a pizza or an ocean wave.

_____

_____

_____

_____

_____

_____

_____

_____

_____

_____

_____

_____

_____

_____

_____

© Pearson Education, Inc., publishing as Pearson Prentice Hall. All rights reserved.

Poetry Collection: Bashō, Anonymous, Lillian Morrison
Support for Extend Your Learning

Research and Technology

Decide which of the three poems you will format, and then use the space below to design your presentation.

Listening and Speaking

Use the lines below to prepare your oral response to one of the poems.

Title of the poem: _____

Form of the poem—for example, haiku, limerick, or concrete: _____

Interpretation of the poem: _____

_____

_____

_____

_____

Evaluation or opinion of the poem: _____

_____

Feedback from the class: _____

_____

_____

_____

_____

_____

© Pearson Education, Inc., publishing as Pearson Prentice Hall. All rights reserved.

Poetry Collection: Bashō, Anonymous, Lillian Morrison
Enrichment: Poetic Art

Artists from all over the world have created sketches that illustrate haiku. Like haiku poetry, haiku art is often simple and spare. It is drawn with a few lines that suggest what the poem says and how it makes the artist feel. Use the space below to create your sketch for "Haiku" by Bashō.

Just as a limerick and a haiku are different in form and spirit, a comic strip is better than a sketch at illustrating a limerick. Draw a four-panel comic strip that shows the action and dialogue in the limerick about the flea, the fly, and the flue. Use both dialogue from the limerick and your own words to illustrate the limerick.

© Pearson Education, Inc., publishing as Pearson Prentice Hall. All rights reserved.

Poetry Collection: Bashō, Anonymous, Lillian Morrison
Selection Test A

Critical Reading *Identify the letter of the choice that best answers the question.*

____ 1. The poem by Bashō is a haiku. How many lines does a haiku contain?
   A. two
   B. three
   C. four
   D. five

____ 2. If you were the frog in Bashō's haiku, which sense would you experience?
   A. the feeling of wetness
   B. the sound of voices
   C. the smell of smoke
   D. the taste of snowflakes

____ 3. Which word best describes the mood of Bashō's haiku ?
   A. love
   B. humor
   C. power
   D. calmness

____ 4. Which is the best paraphrase of this line?
   So they flew through a flaw in the flue.

   A. They flew through the hot chimney.
   B. They flew through a crack in the chimney.
   C. They escaped on a dog named Flue.
   D. They left because someone in the house had the flu.

____ 5. Which description best describes the limerick about the fly and the flea?
   A. It is a serious poem with no rhymes.
   B. It is a love poem without rhymes or rhythm.
   C. It is a funny poem with five lines.
   D. It is a nature poem with three lines.

____ 6. What kind of poem is "The Sidewalk Racer"?
   A. a concrete poem
   B. a limerick
   C. a haiku
   D. a simile

© Pearson Education, Inc., publishing as Pearson Prentice Hall. All rights reserved.

____ 7. What is the shape of the poem "The Sidewalk Racer"?
   A. a sail
   B. the sidewalk
   C. a skateboard
   D. a jet plane

____ 8. In "The Sidewalk Racer," how does the speaker feel?
   A. bored
   B. scared
   C. angry
   D. confident

____ 9. Which statement gives accurate information about "The Sidewalk Racer"?
   A. It uses a unique shape to help describe the thrill of skateboarding.
   B. The speaker in the poem is the skateboard; the listener is the sidewalk.
   C. The speaker uses rhythm and rhyme to make up a song about skateboarding.
   D. Some words in this poem are not as important as other words.

____ 10. When you paraphrase a sentence or a line of poetry, what do you do?
   A. You turn it into a question.
   B. You put it in your own words.
   C. You add humor to it.
   D. You copy it down exactly.

Vocabulary and Grammar

____ 11. Which sentence uses the underlined vocabulary word *incorrectly*?
   A. They had to <u>flee</u> from the fire.
   B. There is a <u>flaw</u> in the window glass.
   C. We saw a <u>flee</u> on our dog.
   D. Your emergency plan has a <u>flaw</u> in it.

____ 12. The flea and the fly had to escape "by hook or by crook." What does this mean?
   A. They had to knife their way out.
   B. They had to get out in any possible way.
   C. They did not trust each other.
   D. They used a hook in the crooked flue.

© Pearson Education, Inc., publishing as Pearson Prentice Hall. All rights reserved.

____ **13.** What is the direct object in this sentence?
The class presented their science projects.

    A. class

    B. their

    C. science

    D. projects

____ **14.** What is the indirect object in this sentence?
Skateboarding gave him a thrill.

    A. Skateboarding

    B. gave

    C. him

    D. thrill

Essay

15. In an essay, describe the setting of Bashō's haiku and "The Sidewalk Racer." Then, tell in which setting you would prefer to spend more time. Explain why would you prefer that setting. Use details from the poem to support your answer.

16. Which poem do you wish you had written—Bashō's haiku, the limerick about the fly and the flea, or Morrison's "The Sidewalk Racer"? In an essay, tell why you would be proud to have written that poem. Use information from the poem in your answer.

© Pearson Education, Inc., publishing as Pearson Prentice Hall. All rights reserved.

Poetry Collection: Bashō, Anonymous, Lillian Morrison
Selection Test B

Critical Reading *Identify the letter of the choice that best completes the statement or answers the question.*

____ 1. Choose the best paraphrase of Bashōs haiku:

An old silent pond . . ./A frog jumps into the pond,/splash! Silence again.

A. The pond was silent until the frog jumped in. Splashing now alternates with quiet.

B. A pond will never be silent after one frog jumps into it and starts splashing around.

C. A frog jumps into a quiet pond; there is a splash; then, all is quiet once more.

D. There was once an ancient body of water that a frog splashed into and died.

____ 2. The haiku form is important for the poem by Bashō because

A. each line has a different syllable count.

B. the haiku form's few words create vivid images of nature.

C. haiku is a Japanese verse form.

D. it is the form of poetry Bashō knew best.

____ 3. What is the number of syllables in each of the three lines of Bashō's haiku?

A. seven, five, seven

B. six, four, six

C. five, six, seven

D. five, seven, five

____ 4. The feeling that the reader gets from Bashō's haiku is best described as

A. excitement and warmth.

B. peacefulness and wonder.

C. power and desolation.

D. patience and humor.

____ 5. The rhythm and rhyme patterns of the limerick form are important because

A. funny poems should have rhyming lines.

B. they make limericks easy to understand.

C. they add to the humor of limericks.

D. they make limericks easy to write.

____ 6. Which lines rhyme in the limerick?

A. first and second lines rhyme, and third and fifth lines rhyme

B. first and third lines rhyme, and second and fifth lines rhyme

C. all the lines rhyme except the last line

D. first, second, and fifth lines rhyme, and third and fourth lines rhyme

© Pearson Education, Inc., publishing as Pearson Prentice Hall. All rights reserved.

____ 7. Choose the best paraphrase of these lines from the limerick.
Said the fly, "Let us flee."/"Let us fly," said the flea./So they flew through a flaw in the flue.
A. The two insects had to get out, so they flew through the chimney even though it was hot.
B. The fly and the flea agreed to escape, so they flew through a crack in the chimney.
C. The flea and the fly agreed that they needed to escape on a dog named Flue.
D. The fly and the flea agreed it was time to leave because the humans in the house had the flu.

____ 8. The limerick about insects is humorous because
A. the insects get out of a bad situation when they work together.
B. the limerick is anonymous.
C. of the tongue-twisting sound effects and meanings of *flea, fly, flue, flee,* and *flaw.*
D. of the irregular rhythm, which adds to the idea that something unexpected will happen.

____ 9. The only true statement about limericks is
A. limericks are usually funny or silly.
B. funny limericks don't have to rhyme.
C. limericks use rhythm but not rhyme.
D. limericks always turn a serious event into a funny one.

____ 10. Which statement best summarizes "The Sidewalk Racer"?
A. The poem uses a unique shape to describe the thrill of skateboarding.
B. The speaker in the poem is the skateboard.
C. The speaker uses rhythm and rhyme to describe skateboarding.
D. Each word is important in this short poem about skateboarding.

____ 11. In "The Sidewalk Racer," the speaker feels
A. bored.
B. hesitant.
C. angry.
D. confident.

____ 12. The concrete form is important to "The Sidewalk Racer" because
A. the poem's shape relates to the subject while catching the reader's eye.
B. skateboards are used on concrete, which could be a form of asphalt.
C. the concrete form is a unique way to write poetry, especially this poem.
D. it is difficult to capture the idea of movement in a poem.

© Pearson Education, Inc., publishing as Pearson Prentice Hall. All rights reserved.

____ 13. Choose the best paraphrase of these lines from "The Sidewalk Racer."
        I'm the one and only/single engine/human auto/mobile.

   A. I wish I could move as fast as a car or a plane, but I can't because I am only
   a human.
   B. I feel as if I am both a single-engine plane and a car.
   C. With my one-engine heart, I am part of my skateboard, moving fast as a car.
   D. Only when I can drive will I be able to move as swiftly and skillfully as I do now.

____ 14. From clues in "The Sidewalk Racer," you can conclude that the speaker
   A. is a professional skateboarder.
   B. enjoys exciting activities.
   C. sails boats, too.
   D. looks forward to driving.

Vocabulary and Grammar

____ 15. Which sentence uses the underlined vocabulary word *incorrectly*?
   A. They had to <u>flee</u> from the storm.
   B. There is one <u>flaw</u> in your argument.
   C. I found a <u>flee</u> on my dog.
   D. That sweater has a <u>flaw</u> in its design.

____ 16. The flea and the fly were caught "between a rock and a hard place," which means
   A. the flue was made of rock.
   B. they were in a difficult situation.
   C. the flaw was hard to fly out of.
   D. they could depend only on themselves.

____ 17. Which word is the direct object in this sentence?
        He enjoyed skateboarding at the park on weekends that summer.

   A. skateboarding
   B. park
   C. weekends
   D. summer

Essay

18. In an essay, compare and contrast any two of the following forms of poetry: concrete,
    haiku, or limerick. Your essay should include a specific description of each of the two
    forms you choose. Explain how the two forms are alike and how they are different. Back
    up your opinions with paraphrases of lines that you can remember from the poems.

19. In an essay, summarize the poem that left the most lasting impression on you: "The
    Sidewalk Racer," Bashō's haiku, or the limerick about the insects. Tell why you found
    this poem to be memorable.

© Pearson Education, Inc., publishing as Pearson Prentice Hall. All rights reserved.

Vocabulary Warm-up Word Lists

Study these words from the poems. Then, apply your knowledge to the activities that follow.

Word List A

dish [DISH] *n.* a bowl; a container used to serve food
  This <u>dish</u> is for the cat's food and that one is for the dog's food.

forest [FAWR ist] *n.* area of land covered in trees
  The <u>forest</u> is dark because the trees are blocking out the sunlight.

paw [PAW] *n.* name for the foot of an animal
  The dog is limping because it hurt its <u>paw</u>.

spring [SPRING] *n.* place where water rises out of the ground
  That hole in the ground with water running out of it is a natural <u>spring</u>.

stripes [STRYPS] *n.* long, narrow bands of color
  The white wall is boring; let's paint some blue <u>stripes</u> on it.

whisker [WIS kuhr] *n.* long stiff hair that grows out of a person's or an animal's face
  There's more than one <u>whisker</u> on each side of a cat's face.

Word List B

accidents [AK si duhnts] *n.* unplanned events that cause people to be hurt or things to be damaged
  Many car <u>accidents</u> happen when the roads are wet and slippery.

fatal [FAYT uhl] *adj.* causing someone to die
  Her injury wasn't <u>fatal</u>; she just broke a few bones.

fellow [FEL loh] *n.* a boy or man
  He's a good <u>fellow</u> who never lies or cheats.

howl [HOWL] *v.* make a roaring, screaming, or whining noise
  When the dogs <u>howl</u> like that, it hurts my ears.

rage [RAYJ] *v.* burst of anger
  She's in a <u>rage</u> about losing the game; I've never seen her so mad.

wintry [WIN tree] *n.* cold winterlike
  I always wear a hat, scarf, and gloves in this <u>wintry</u> weather.

© Pearson Education, Inc., publishing as Pearson Prentice Hall. All rights reserved.

Poetry Collection: Soseki, Anonymous, and Dorthi Charles
Vocabulary Warm-up Exercises

Exercise A *Fill in each blank in the paragraph below with an appropriate word from Word List A. Use each word only once.*

Before her hike, Dee ate a large breakfast, including two eggs and a big

[1] _____ of oatmeal. Then she put on her warmest sweater, the

yellow one with orange [2] _____. Once she entered the woods, Dee

was happy to have done so. The [3] _____ was freezing. Even the

[4] _____ was frozen; not a drop of water ran out of it. The hike ended

when Dee saw a [5] _____ print in the snow and got scared. Dee didn't

want to run into a bear so she ran back to her car. She still felt a little nervous when she

got home, and jumped when she felt a [6] _____ brush against her leg.

Looking down, she saw that it was just her cat, Lil. "You're the kind of wild animal

I like," Dee said.

Exercise B *Find a synonym for each word in the following vocabulary list. Use each synonym in a sentence that makes the meaning of the word clear.*

Example: vocabulary word: *autumn*   synonym: *fall*
    sentence: *I like fall better than winter because it's less cold.*

1. accidents

   _____

2. fatal

   _____

3. fellow

   _____

4. howl

   _____

5. rage

   _____

6. wintry

   _____

© Pearson Education, Inc., publishing as Pearson Prentice Hall. All rights reserved.

Name _____ Date _____

Read the following passage. Pay special attention to the underlined words. Then, read it again, and complete the activities. Use a separate sheet of paper for your written answers.

Nature programs showing big cats in the wild are always fun to watch. Usually when people watch them, they are amazed at how similar the big cats are to the cats they keep at home. Lions, tigers, pumas, and leopards do resemble ordinary housecats in a number of ways.

The expressions and behavior of big cats remind people of their own pets. One example is the way a lion twitches a <u>whisker</u>, the long, stiff hair that sticks out from a cat's face. It seems like something that happens a hundred times a day at home. So does the way a big cat cleans itself with its tongue. So does the way it scratches at a tree with its <u>paw</u>.

A preference for nighttime activity is another similarity. Pet owners are used to watching their cats nap for most of the day. Most big cats share this habit of taking it easy when the sun is out. Daytime is for resting. When the sun goes down, it's the time to get more active.

Of course, there are many differences between big cats and housecats. These differences go beyond the color of the <u>stripes</u> in their fur. Size is one of them. Big cats are many times larger than housecats. The average pet cat weighs about ten pounds. A puma, though, can weigh 200 pounds. The lion is known as king of the <u>forest</u> for a reason. Few other animals walking in the woods can reach four or five hundred pounds.

Unlike housecats, big cats in the wild don't get dinner served to them in a <u>dish</u>. Big cats are carnivores. They eat other animals. They must hunt if they are hungry. They must also search for sources of water. They can find it in a lake, a river, or a mountain <u>spring</u>.

1. Underline the words that tell the meaning of <u>whisker</u>. Then, name another animal that would have a *whisker*.

2. Circle the words that tell what a big cat can do with a <u>paw</u>. Then, tell what *paw* means.

3. Circle the words that tell where big cats and housecats have <u>stripes</u>. Then, tell what *stripes* means.

4. Circle the nearby word that has the same meaning as <u>forest</u>. Then, use the word *forest* in a sentence.

5. Underline the words that tell what housecats get served in a <u>dish</u>. Then, tell what *dish* means.

6. Underline the words that tell what cats can get from a <u>spring</u>. Then, write a sentence using the word *spring*.

© Pearson Education, Inc., publishing as Pearson Prentice Hall. All rights reserved.
129

Poetry Collection: Soseki, Anonymous, and Dorthi Charles
Reading Warm-up B

Read the following passage. Pay special attention to the underlined words. Then, read it again, and complete the activities. Use a separate sheet of paper for your written answers.

Tim had driven West Virginia's winding roads for three decades, yet he'd never seen them like this before. He'd experienced all kinds of <u>wintry</u> conditions, ice storms, and freezing rain, but this past week of blizzards was the worst period of severe weather he'd ever encountered. Storm after storm dumped snow on the area. The winds were so strong that they could knock down a grown man. They almost seemed angry, as if they were in some kind of <u>rage</u>.

The roads were almost impossible to drive on; any smart person would stay away from driving conditions like these. Tim, however, didn't have a choice. As a police officer, he had to patrol the roads and make sure that no one got into trouble.

There had been many <u>accidents</u> in the early part of the week. Though the roads were deadly, none of the crashes were <u>fatal</u>. There weren't many injuries, just lots of dented bumpers and doors.

Now people realized how dangerous it was to drive, and Tim scarcely saw anyone outside. Once in a while he glanced at a figure of someone outside a house, taking a break from endless snow shoveling.

As Tim drove through the steep hills on the edge of town, he thought he saw tire marks leading from the side of the road and pulled over to take a look. Sure enough, there was a car about twenty yards down the hill, stuck sideways in the snow. Tim ran down the hill, looked through the window and saw the driver. He wasn't conscious; his head was pressed against the wheel. When Tim pulled him out of the car, however, he heard the driver <u>howl</u> in pain. Tim carried him back to his cruiser and drove him to the hospital. Doctors considered the <u>fellow</u> very fortunate. Thanks to Tim's help, the man recovered quickly.

1. Underline the words that name a few <u>wintry</u> conditions. Then, tell what *wintry* means.

2. Circle the words that tell what seems to be in a <u>rage</u>. Then, tell how a person feels when he or she is in a *rage*.

3. Circle the words that tell when there had been many <u>accidents</u>. Then, tell what *accidents* means.

4. Underline the nearby word that has nearly the same meaning as <u>fatal</u>. Then, describe something that can be *fatal*.

5. Circle the word that tells what makes the driver <u>howl</u>. Then, tell what *howl* means.

6. Underline the nearby word that has the same meaning as <u>fellow</u>. Then, list three other words with similar meanings as *fellow*.

© Pearson Education, Inc., publishing as Pearson Prentice Hall. All rights reserved.

Name _____ Date _____

Reading: Reread to Paraphrase

Paraphrasing is restating an author's words in your own words. Paraphrasing difficult or confusing passages in a poem helps you clarify the meaning. Use these steps to help you:

- First, stop and reread any difficult lines or passages.
- Next, identify unfamiliar words. Find their meaning and replace them with words that mean the same or nearly the same thing.
- In a concrete poem, words are shaped to reflect the subject of the poem.
- Finally, reread the lines to see if your paraphrase makes sense in the poem.

A chart such as the one below can be useful in helping you paraphrase.

DIRECTIONS: *In the left column of the chart are passages from the poems in this collection. Underline unfamiliar words. Find the meanings of these words and write the meanings in the second column. In the third column, paraphrase the passage. The first one has been done for you as an example.*

Passage	New Words	Paraphrase
Example: winds <u>howl</u> in a <u>rage</u>	howl: make a loud wailing cry; rage: great anger	winds are so strong that they make a loud crying noise, like an angry person
1. with no leaves to blow.		
2. There was a young fellow named Hall,		
3. Who fell in the spring in the fall;		

© Pearson Education, Inc., publishing as Pearson Prentice Hall. All rights reserved.

Poetry Collection: Soseki, Anonymous, Dorthi Charles
Literary Analysis: Forms of Poetry

Poets use different **forms of poetry** suited to the ideas, images, and feelings they want to express. The following are three poetic forms:

- A **haiku** is a Japanese verse form with three lines. Line 1 has five syllables, line 2 has seven syllables, and line 3 has five syllables. Haiku often focuses on nature. It tries to capture a moment by giving you a few quick images, or word-pictures, that help you see, hear, and feel something in a new way.
- A **limerick** is a short, funny poem of five lines. The first, second, and fifth lines rhyme and have three beats, or stressed syllables. The third and fourth lines rhyme and have two strong beats.
- In a **concrete poem,** words are arranged in a shape that reflects the subject of the poem.

DIRECTIONS: *Answer the questions about each form of poetry below.*

1. "Haiku" by Soseki

	What do you see?	What do you hear?	What do you feel?
Over the wintry			
forest, winds howl in a rage			
with no leaves to blow.			

2. "Limerick" by Anonymous

    Underline each *stressed* syllable in each line. Then, identify the rhyme scheme or pattern by writing the letters *a* or *b* at the end of each line. Give each rhyme a different letter. For example, write the letter *a* at the end of the first line and *a* at the end of each line that rhymes with line one.

    There was a young fellow named Hall, _____

    Who fell in the spring in the fall; _____

       'Twould have been a sad thing _____

       If he'd died in the spring, _____

    But he didn't—he died in the fall. _____

3. "Concrete Cat" by Dorthi Charles

    Concrete means "something that can be touched," such as a tree or a cell phone.

    _____

    _____

    _____

© Pearson Education, Inc., publishing as Pearson Prentice Hall. All rights reserved.

Poetry Collection: Soseki, Anonymous, Dorthi Charles
Vocabulary Builder

Word List

howl	rage	fellow

A. DIRECTIONS: *In the limerick below, fill in each blank with the correct vocabulary word.*

A silly young _____ named Phil

Used to _____ at the moon on the hill

So a wolf in a _____

Shut Phil up in a cage

'Til Phil made a vow to be still.

B. DIRECTIONS: *A word map can help you explore the meaning of a word. Make a word map for each vocabulary word. The first one has been started for you.*

1.

Definition: fury, wrath	**RAGE**	**Synonym:**

Sentence: Beth goes into a rage when her sister borrows her clothes.

2.

Definition:	**HOWL**	**Synonym:**

Sentence:

3.

Definition:	**FELLOW**	**Synonym:**

Sentence:

© Pearson Education, Inc., publishing as Pearson Prentice Hall. All rights reserved.

Name _____ Date _____

Support for Writing a Poem

You have read examples of a haiku, a limerick, and a concrete poem. Now, try writing a poem of your own, using one of these forms.

What form of poetry will you use? _____

What do you need to remember about this form? Take notes here.

_____

_____

_____

_____

_____

Use the lines below to jot down ideas for your poem. If you're writing a haiku, you will want to think about nature images. If you're writing a limerick, think up a silly character or start with place names that sound funny and will be easy to rhyme—for example, "Chicago." If you're writing a concrete poem, think of a real subject that suggests a shape—for example, a pizza or an ocean wave.

_____

_____

_____

_____

_____

_____

_____

_____

_____

_____

_____

_____

_____

_____

© Pearson Education, Inc., publishing as Pearson Prentice Hall. All rights reserved.

Name _____ Date _____

Research and Technology

Decide which of the three poems you will format, and then use the space below to design your presentation.

Listening and Speaking

Use the lines below to prepare your oral response to one of the poems.

Title of the poem: _____

Form of the poem—for example, haiku, limerick, or concrete: _____

Interpretation of the poem: _____

_____

_____

_____

_____

Evaluation or opinion of the poem: _____

_____

Feedback from the class: _____

_____

_____

_____

_____

_____

© Pearson Education, Inc., publishing as Pearson Prentice Hall. All rights reserved.
135

Poetry Collection: Soseki, Anonymous, Dorthi Charles
Enrichment: Poetic Art

Artists from all over the world have created sketches that illustrate haiku. Like haiku poetry, haiku art is often simple and spare. It is drawn with a few lines that suggest what the poem says and how it makes the artist feel. Use the space below to create your sketch for "Haiku" by Soseki.

Just as a limerick and a haiku are different in form and spirit, a comic strip is better than a sketch at illustrating a limerick. Draw a four-panel comic strip that shows the action in the limerick about the young fellow named Hall. You may want to invent some dialogue for Hall or you may want to use one or two lines of the limerick as captions, or titles, under each panel.

Poetry Collections: Bashō, Anonymous, Lillian Morrison;
Soseki, Anonymous, Dorthi Charles
Build Language Skills: Vocabulary

Idioms

Idioms are word phrases with meanings that are very different from the combined dictionary meanings of the words in the phrase. People use idioms when they speak informally.

Mr. Sanchez asked us to **cut out** the noise.

The dictionary, or literal, meaning of *cut out* is "to separate or remove with a knife."

The idiomatic meaning of *cut out* is "stop" (stop doing something that is annoying).

The dictionary definition of the most important word in the idiom will often provide definitions of idioms that contain the word. A word like *cut* may be included in several idioms. *Cut and dried*, meaning "dull or uninteresting," is an example of another idiom that uses *cut*.

A. DIRECTIONS: *Write the idiomatic meaning of each phrase. If you don't know the meaning, try to find it by looking up the important word in a dictionary.*

1. chill out _____
2. catch some Zs _____
3. keep an eye on _____
4. burn the midnight oil _____

Academic Vocabulary Practice

convey	explain	paraphrase	passage	represent

B. DIRECTIONS: *Circle* T *if the statement is true or* F *if the statement is false. Then, explain your answer.*

1. It is possible to *convey* the main idea of a narrative poem in one word.

   T / F _____

2. To *explain* the meaning of a haiku will require more words than the haiku.

   T / F _____

3. When you *paraphrase* a poem, you use rhyme and rhythm.

   T / F _____

4. If a *passage* of a poem is difficult, you should stop and reread it.

   T / F _____

5. When you discuss an author's ideas, it is important to *represent* them correctly.

   T / F _____

© Pearson Education, Inc., publishing as Pearson Prentice Hall. All rights reserved.

Poetry Collections: Bashō, Anonymous, Lillian Morrison;
Soseki, Anonymous, Dorthi Charles

Build Language Skills: Grammar

Subject Complements: Direct and Indirect Objects

Most sentences need words beyond a subject and a verb to complete their meaning. Direct objects and indirect objects complete ideas and make sentences more specific.

- A **direct object** is a noun or pronoun that receives the action of the verb and answers the question *Whom?* or *What?*
- They recited their <u>poems</u>. *What* was recited? their poems

  Poems receives the action of the verb *recited*.
- The teacher greeted <u>them</u>. Greeted *whom?* them

  Them receives the action of the verb *greeted*.

- An **indirect object** is a noun or pronoun that names the person or thing to whom or for whom an action is done. An indirect object answers the question *To or for whom?* or *To or for what?*
- She sent <u>him</u> a poem. *To whom?* him *What?* a poem

  The indirect object is *him*.

  The direct object is *poem*.

- He wrote his <u>grandmother</u> and <u>grandfather</u> a limerick. *For whom?* grandmother and grandfather *What?* a limerick

  The compound indirect object is *grandmother* and *grandfather*.

  The direct object is *limerick*.

A. PRACTICE: *Underline the <u>direct object</u> once. Underline the <u>indirect object</u> twice. Then, write the question each object answers:* • What? • To whom? • For whom?

1. The new student gave the teacher his haiku.

   Direct object answers _____ Indirect object answers_____

2. The nurse offered Sally a cell phone.

   Direct object answers _____ Indirect object answers _____

3. Her mother sent the teacher a note about Sally's absence from school.

   Direct object answers _____ Indirect object answers _____

B. Writing Application: *Write four sentences about a shopping trip. Tell what you and an adult family member buy for you and others. Include a direct object and an indirect object in every sentence. Underline the direct objects once and the indirect objects twice. You may want to use some of the following verbs:* bought, gave, showed, paid, sold, asked, found.

_____

_____

_____

© Pearson Education, Inc., publishing as Pearson Prentice Hall. All rights reserved.

Poetry Collection: Soseki, Anonymous, Dorthi Charles
Selection Test A

Critical Reading *Identify the letter of the choice that best answers the question.*

____ 1. What season of the year does Soseki's haiku describe?
    A. autumn
    B. winter
    C. spring
    D. summer

____ 2. According to Soseki's haiku, how does the wind feel when no leaves are left to blow away?
    A. angry
    B. lonely
    C. relieved
    D. sad

____ 3. How do you paraphrase a line of poetry?
    A. You put it into your own words.
    B. You change it into a question.
    C. You copy it exactly.
    D. You take out the phrases in it.

____ 4. Which is the best paraphrase of this line?

    winds howl in a rage

    A. Anger can sound like the wind, or it can sound like howling.
    B. What kind of angry sound does the wind make?
    C. Winds make a loud, crying noise, like a very angry person.
    D. Winds howl in a rage.

____ 5. How many lines does a haiku poem contain?
    A. two
    B. three
    C. five
    D. six

____ 6. Which statement about the limerick form is true?
    A. Limericks do not have to rhyme.
    B. Limericks are poems about nature.
    C. Limericks always include serious subjects.
    D. Limericks are short and funny.

© Pearson Education, Inc., publishing as Pearson Prentice Hall. All rights reserved.

_____ 7. Which word best describes the limerick about Hall's accident?

    A. angry

    B. anxious

    C. sad

    D. silly

_____ 8. What is the poetic form of "Concrete Cat"?

    A. concrete

    B. limerick

    C. haiku

    D. like a cat

_____ 9. Which statement gives accurate information about "Concrete Cat"?

    A. It is not really a poem; it is, instead, a work of art.

    B. It is a poem that has no words.

    C. The speaker in the poem is a cat who has killed a mouse.

    D. It uses a unique shape that shows the subject of the poem.

_____ 10. What is the best paraphrase of the word *mouse* as it appears in "Concrete Cat"?

    A. The mouse is sneaking up on the cat.

    B. The word *mouse* is upside down because the mouse is dead.

    C. The word *mouse* does not have a mouse shape.

    D. The word *mouse* was the last thing added to the poem because it appears at the end.

_____ 11. How would you describe what the cat looks like in "Concrete Cat"?

    A. It is a kitten.

    B. It is all one color.

    C. It is striped.

    D. It has spots.

Vocabulary and Grammar

_____ 12. Which sentence uses an underlined vocabulary word *incorrectly*?

    A. When Grandma was young, no girl would ask a <u>fellow</u> to a dance.

    B. The wolves keep us awake when they <u>howl</u> at night.

    C. Spring breezes moved in a gentle <u>rage</u> through the trees.

    D. That <u>fellow</u> who rarely gets angry was in a <u>rage</u> about high gas prices.

© Pearson Education, Inc., publishing as Pearson Prentice Hall. All rights reserved.

___ **13.** What is the indirect object in this sentence?

Hall's ending brought him fame.

A. Hall's

B. ending

C. him

D. fame

Essay

14. Choose one of the poetic forms in this collection—haiku, limerick, or concrete poem. In an essay, describe three things about that poetic form that make it different from other kinds of poems. Include at least one detail from Soseki's haiku, the limerick about Hall's accident, or "Concrete Cat" to support any of the three points you make.

15. If you could write a book of poems, all of which would be in only one poetic form—haiku, limerick, or concrete poetry—which form would you choose? In an essay, identify one form and give at least two reasons for your choice.

Poetry Collection: Soseki, Anonymous, Dorthi Charles
Selection Test B

Critical Reading *Identify the letter of the choice that best completes the statement or answers the question.*

____ 1. Soseki's haiku describes what is happening in the winter
    A. by the sea.
    B. in the woods.
    C. in a city.
    D. during a war.

____ 2. Choose the best paraphrase of these two lines of Soseki's haiku.
    Over the wintry
    forest, winds howl in a rage
    A. In winter, winds blast through the forest.
    B. The wind sounds angry in winter.
    C. In the winter forest, winds roar in anger.
    D. Nothing howls except wind in the forest.

____ 3. How many syllables are in each line of Soseki's haiku?
    A. five, six, seven
    B. seven, five, seven
    C. six, four, six
    D. five, seven, five

____ 4. The feelings that one gets from reading Soseki's haiku are best described as
    A. power/frustration/desolation.
    B. peace/warmth/love.
    C. calmness/wonder/beauty.
    D. patience/wisdom/rebirth.

____ 5. The rhyme and rhythm patterns of the limerick form are important because
    A. a funny poem has to have rhyming lines.
    B. they make a limerick easy to understand.
    C. they make a limerick easy to write.
    D. they add to the silliness of the limerick.

____ 6. The lines that rhyme in the limerick about the accident are
    A. first and second; third and fifth.
    B. first and third; second and fifth.
    C. all the lines.
    D. first, second, fifth; third and fourth.

© Pearson Education, Inc., publishing as Pearson Prentice Hall. All rights reserved.

_____ 7. Choose the best paraphrase of these two lines of the limerick.

There was a young fellow named Hall

Who fell in the spring in the fall;

    A. A thief named Hall fell in the spring.

    B. A boy named Hall fell into a pool of water in autumn.

    C. Who fell into the well? Was it young Hall? When did it happen?

    D. A juvenile male named Hall suffered an accident when he fell into a stream or river.

_____ 8. The limerick about the accident is humorous because

    A. some words have double meanings.

    B. the limerick is anonymous.

    C. Hall survives a bad accident.

    D. something unexpected happens.

_____ 9. In the limerick about the accident, Hall has his accident during the

    A. spring.

    B. summer.

    C. fall.

    D. winter.

_____ 10. The concrete poetic form is important to "Concrete Cat" because

    A. the poem is shaped like its subject.

    B. the poem tells about cats in the city.

    C. the poem tells about a cat sculpture.

    D. concrete means "real or solid."

_____ 11. "Concrete Cat" is a poem that appeals mostly to

    A. the eyes.

    B. the ears.

    C. the mind.

    D. all the senses.

_____ 12. The feeling that one gets from "Concrete Cat" might best be described as

    A. powerful.

    B. comical.

    C. sad.

    D. curious.

_____ 13. The word mouse is upside down most probably because the poet is suggesting that

    A. the mouse is dead.

    B. the cat is more important than the mouse.

    C. the cat has not noticed the mouse.

    D. the mouse is hiding under the cat's tail.

© Pearson Education, Inc., publishing as Pearson Prentice Hall. All rights reserved.

____ 14. In "Concrete Cat," the best "paraphrase" of the cat's ears in this concrete poem is
   A. they stand up on each side of the cat's head.
   B. the word *ear* is shaped like two ears on the cat's head; capital *A* stands for the ear tips.
   C. they are spelled *e-a-r* and they come out from above the cat's eyes.
   D. they cannot really hear because they are made of letters; they are not real cat's ears.

Vocabulary and Grammar

____ 15. Which sentence uses an underlined vocabulary word *incorrectly*?
   A. The police took away that <u>fellow</u> who was screaming with <u>rage</u>.
   B. A <u>howl</u> of disappointment broke out when the football went under the goalpost.
   C. A gentle summer breeze blew in a <u>rage</u> through the park.
   D. We hear the wolves when they <u>howl</u> at night.

____ 16. In the limerick, the character Hall "bit the dust" which means that Hall
   A. got sick.
   B. choked on dust.
   C. had allergies.
   D. died.

____ 17. What is the direct object in this sentence?
   His fall gave Hall a sad end in the spring.

   A. fall
   B. Hall
   C. end
   D. spring

Essay

18. Which of the three poems in this collection—Soseki's haiku, the anonymous limerick, or "Concrete Cat"—is the most difficult to paraphrase? Which poem is the easiest to paraphrase? In an essay, explain why you think some poetic forms are more difficult to paraphrase than others.

19. If you were a poet, would you prefer to be known as a famous writer of haiku, limericks, or concrete poems? Choose one of these poetic forms and explain in an essay why you would prefer to write that form of poetry. Base your decision on the type of poem you like best and the poetic form you think might be the most interesting to write. Use details from the poems in this collection to support your reasons.

Vocabulary Warm-up Word Lists

Study these words from the poetry of Shel Silverstein, Octavio Paz, and Rachel Field. Then, apply your knowledge to the activities that follow.

Word List A

allergies [AL uhr jeez] *n.* exaggerated bodily reactions, such as sneezing or itching, to a substance or thing that does not bother most people
    The spring pollen gave Lucas <u>allergies</u> that made him sneeze.

clawed [KLAWD] *v.* dug or scraped at something with claws or fingernails
    The cat <u>clawed</u> a hole in the chair.

disappear [dis uh PEER] *v.* to vanish from sight
    Marisol wanted to <u>disappear</u> from the spotlight and never be seen again.

dispersed [dis PUHRST] *v.* went away in different directions
    Once the show was over, the crowd <u>dispersed</u> into the night.

meowing [me OW ing] *n.* the sound a cat makes
    The loud <u>meowing</u> of the hungry cat woke Judy up.

scratched [SKRACHT] *v.* scraped or very shallowly cut
    Luis ran into a rosebush and was <u>scratched</u> by the thorns on the branches.

Word List B

beating [BEET ing] *adj.* having natural, short rhythmical movements
    The doctor examined the sound of my <u>beating</u> heart.

beneath [bee NEETH] *prep.* under or lower than
    Peter liked to feel the grass <u>beneath</u> his bare feet.

developed [di VEL uhpt] *v.* got something gradually
    Rita came down with the flu and <u>developed</u> a bad cough.

hollowed [HAHL ohd] *v.* created a hole in the center of something
    Chang <u>hollowed</u> out the center of the pumpkin by removing the seeds inside.

motionless [MOH shuhn lis] *adj.* not moving
    The car sat <u>motionless</u> in the driveway.

sculpted [SKUHLP ted] *v.* carved or created a three-dimensional object
    The artist <u>sculpted</u> a work of art in clay.

© Pearson Education, Inc., publishing as Pearson Prentice Hall. All rights reserved.

Poetry Collection: Shel Silverstein, Octavio Paz, and Rachel Field
Vocabulary Warm-up Exercises

Exercise A *Fill in each blank in the paragraph below with an appropriate word from Word List A. Use each word only once.*

Randi went to visit the cat shelter. She could hear the [1] _____ of the cats from outside the building. There were so many strays! Randi hoped that the cats would be [2] _____ to good homes some day.

Inside, Randi sneezed. Her [3] _____ were bothering her again. Her favorite cat, Gus, ran his paw against his cage and [4] _____ at its door. When Randi went to let him out, Gus [5] _____ her. Randi looked at the small scrape on her hand. Then she realized Gus had run away.

"Gus," she called out to him, "Did you [6] _____?" She soon found him hiding underneath a cage.

Exercise B *Revise each sentence so that the underlined vocabulary word is used in a logical way. Be sure to keep the vocabulary word in your revision.*

Example: Anna's rapidly <u>beating</u> heart was silent and had no rhythm.
Anna's rapidly beating heart made a rhythmic, pounding sound.

1. The artist <u>sculpted</u> the two-dimensional painting on a piece of paper.
_____

2. The teacher took the right medicine and quickly <u>developed</u> a nasty cough.
_____

3. The actor on the stage appeared <u>motionless</u> when he ran around singing.
_____

4. I reached <u>beneath</u> my desk to place my book on top of it.
_____

5. The baker <u>hollowed</u> out a loaf of bread by filling it with a spicy meat stuffing.
_____

© Pearson Education, Inc., publishing as Pearson Prentice Hall. All rights reserved.

Name _____ Date _____

Read the following passage. Pay special attention to the underlined words. Then, read it again, and complete the activities. Use a separate sheet of paper for your written answers.

Have you ever been to an animal shelter? Shelters house homeless or unwanted dogs, cats, and other animals. The goal of many shelters is to see that these animals are <u>dispersed</u> into new homes. The shelters want to give them to people who will love and take care of the animals as pets. If you want a new pet, a shelter might be just the place to find one.

The inside of an animal shelter can be quite noisy and crowded. Shelters are filled with sounds like the barking of dogs and the <u>meowing</u> of cats. Until a home can be found for them, the animals are kept in cages indoors, or in fenced-in areas outside. Animals in outdoor pens may try to dig through the dirt with their claws to come out on the other side of the fence. Some animals in shelters have <u>clawed</u> their way out of such pens. If an animal escapes, it could <u>disappear</u> and never be found again.

If you visit an animal shelter, you must be careful not to get <u>scratched</u> by a cat or dog when you greet or pet them. Some of the animals are not used to friendly people and may scratch you because they are afraid of you. However, most of the animals are friendly and are ready to be brought into a loving home.

Do you want to take an animal home from an animal shelter? If so, it is important to answer these questions. First of all, can you provide the animal with a good home? Will your family let you keep the animal? Does anyone in your family have <u>allergies</u> to the animal you want? These bodily reactions can cause someone to sneeze every time they get near your pet.

Once you are ready for a new pet, contact your local animal shelter. The people who work there will be happy to help you find an animal to take home.

1. Underline the words that tell what happens when the animals are <u>dispersed</u>. Then, tell what *dispersed* means.

2. Circle the word that helps explain what <u>meowing</u> is. Do you like the sound of *meowing*? Why or why not?

3. Circle the phrase that explains <u>clawed</u>. Then, write a sentence using the word *clawed*.

4. Circle the phrase that tells you what it means to <u>disappear</u>. Then, define *disappear* in your own words.

5. Underline the phrase that tells why you may be <u>scratched</u> by an animal in a shelter. Has anything ever *scratched* you? Explain.

6. Underline the words that describe <u>allergies</u>. Then, use the word *allergies* in a sentence.

© Pearson Education, Inc., publishing as Pearson Prentice Hall. All rights reserved.

Poetry Collection: Shel Silverstein, Octavio Paz, and Rachel Field
Reading Warm-up B

Read the following passage. Pay special attention to the underlined words. Then, read it again, and complete the activities. Use a separate sheet of paper for your written answers.

Which seems stronger, water or rock? While the obvious answer might be rock, water can actually wear away at rock. This process is called erosion. Erosion is the gradual wearing down of land or stone by water or wind.

Water erosion happens over a long period of time. It can take millions of years. The force of water slowly removes tiny fragments from stone. Because stone is motionless, it cannot escape the friction of the water. The water flows as the stone stands still, and this puts pressure upon the stone. This water pressure removes tiny pieces of stone. If a rough piece of stone is exposed to water for a long enough time, it will be sculpted smooth. The water will shape the stone.

Riverbeds are created through water erosion. If the same stream of water runs across land or stone for a long enough time, the water will cut a path through it. Beneath the river, the land and stone of the riverbed will be carried away by the river's current. As time goes by, the riverbed will deepen. A swiftly moving river with a lot of water pressure will have developed a deep riverbed.

The Grand Canyon is an example of a riverbed created through water erosion. Over millions of years, the flowing Colorado River dug a deep pit through the center of its riverbed. It hollowed out one of the most spectacular canyons in the world. The relentless, beating pressure of the Colorado River wore down stone to create the walls of the Grand Canyon. This continuous, rhythmic pressure slowly created a gorge by wearing away the colored rock canyon walls.

Next time you pass a river or a stream, pick up a stone. Does it have smooth edges or rough ones? If the edges are smooth, you can tell that the stone has been worn away through water erosion.

1. Underline the words that help explain the word motionless. Then, tell what *motionless* means.

2. Circle the words that describe the word sculpted. Then, use *sculpted* in a sentence.

3. Underline the words that tell you what is beneath the river. Then, write a sentence about what is *beneath* you right now.

4. Underline the words that tell what a swiftly moving river will have developed. Write a sentence using the word *developed*.

5. Circle the sentence that explains how the Colorado River hollowed out the canyon. Then, tell what *hollowed* means.

6. Underline the words that help explain the word beating. Then, write a sentence using *beating*.

© Pearson Education, Inc., publishing as Pearson Prentice Hall. All rights reserved.

Poetry Collection: Shel Silverstein, Octavio Paz, Rachel Field
Reading: Read Aloud According to Punctuation to Paraphrase

Paraphrasing is restating something in your own words. To paraphrase a poem, you must first understand it and then use simpler language to restate its meaning. **Reading aloud according to punctuation** will help you find clues to a poem's meaning.

- When you read a poem aloud, do not automatically stop at the end of each line.
- Pause only at punctuation marks, as if you were reading a prose passage.

Even when you read poetry silently to yourself, it will make more sense if you follow these rules:

- **No punctuation** at the ends of lines: don't stop
- **After a comma (,):** slight pause
- **After a colon (:), semicolon (;), or dash (—):** longer pause
- **After endmarks—a period (.), question mark (?), or exclamation point (!):** full stop

A. DIRECTIONS: *Below are the first six lines from the poem "Parade." For each line, write the letters* SP *for slight pause,* LP *for longer pause,* FS *for full stop, or* DS *for don't stop. The first line has been done for you as an example.*

Line 1: This is the day the circus comes   <u>DS</u>
Line 2: With blare of brass, with beating drums,   _____
Line 3: And clashing cymbals, and with roar   _____
Line 4: Of wild beasts never heard before   _____
Line 5: Within town limits. _____ Spick and span _____
Line 6: Will shine each gilded cage and van;   _____

B. DIRECTIONS: *Briefly explain why a good reader will not pause between lines 3 and 4.*

_____

_____

_____

_____

_____

_____

_____

_____

_____

_____

_____

© Pearson Education, Inc., publishing as Pearson Prentice Hall. All rights reserved.

Poetry Collection: Shel Silverstein, Octavio Paz, Rachel Field
Literary Analysis: Sound Devices

Sound devices are a writer's tools for bringing out the music in words and for expressing feelings. Sound devices commonly used in poetry include the following:

- **Repetition:** the use, more than once, of any element of language—a sound, word, phrase, clause, or sentence—as in *give me liberty, or give me death*
- **Alliteration:** the repetition of initial consonant sounds, such as the *r* sound in *rock 'n' roll* or the *sl* sound in *slipping and sliding*
- **Onomatopoeia:** the use of a word that sounds like what it means, such as *roar* and *buzz*

A. DIRECTIONS: *Underline the repetition, alliteration, and onomatopoeia in the following lines from the poetry collection. On the line after each item, write R for repetition, A for alliteration, and O for onomatopoeia. Some items will have more than one letter. The first one has been done for you.*

1. I've been <u>scratched and sprayed and bitten</u>   R, A
2. No more midnight meowing mews   _____
3. Water and wind and stone   _____
4. the water murmurs as it goes   _____
5. With blare of brass, with beating drums,   _____
6. And clashing cymbals, and with roar   _____

B. DIRECTIONS: *Find one example of repetition, one example of alliteration, and one example of onomatopoeia in this passage. Then, write the examples on the lines below.*

When we started feeding the feral cat, we did not know she was about to have kittens. When the kittens were born, they were very tiny. As they grew older, their purring sounded like a motorboat. Like squeaky, funny balls of fluff, they chased each other, pounced on each other, and raced with each other. We were lucky to find homes for them—and we kept Felicity, the feral cat, who is now as tame as tame can be.

1. Example of repetition: _____
2. Example of alliteration: _____
3. Example of onomatopoeia: _____

© Pearson Education, Inc., publishing as Pearson Prentice Hall. All rights reserved.

Name _____ Date _____

Vocabulary Builder

Word List

| dispersed   murmurs   leisurely |

A. DIRECTIONS: *Circle* T *if the statement is true or* F *if the statement is false. Then, explain your answer.*

1. If thunder *dispersed* children playing in the park, the children would quickly return.

   T / F _____

2. If a student *murmurs* answers to a teacher's questions, the teacher will hear them well.

   T / F _____

3. If a young child is moving in a *leisurely* way before school, he will miss the school bus.

   T / F _____

B. DIRECTIONS: *Following the instructions, use each Word List word correctly.*

1. Use *dispersed* in a sentence about an election at school.

   _____

   _____

2. Use *murmurs* in a sentence about a conversation you might hear in a restaurant.

   _____

   _____

3. Use *leisurely* in a sentence about what might happen on a weekend.

   _____

   _____

C. DIRECTIONS: *Write the letter of the word that means the* opposite *of the word in* CAPITAL LETTERS.

____ 1. DISPERSED
   A. drove off   **B.** disposed   **C.** gathered   **D.** neglected

____ 2. MURMURS
   A. shouts   **B.** whispers   **C.** laughs   **D.** cries

____ 3. LEISURELY
   A. calm   **B.** unfair   **C.** angry   **D.** quick

© Pearson Education, Inc., publishing as Pearson Prentice Hall. All rights reserved.

Name _____ Date _____

Support for Writing a Prose Description

Use the chart to create your list of details for your prose description of the picture that the poet painted. This list will help you focus on details that appeal to the senses.

Details I Might See:

Details I Might Smell:

Details I Might Hear:

Details I Might Touch or Be Able to Feel:

Details I Might Taste:

Now, use the details you have collected to write your prose description.

© Pearson Education, Inc., publishing as Pearson Prentice Hall. All rights reserved.

Poetry Collection: Shel Silverstein, Octavio Paz, Rachel Field
Support for Extend Your Learning

Research and Technology

Use the chart to record the facts for the résumé of the poet you have chosen.

Name of Poet: _____

Personal Information (birthplace, childhood, family, travel, hobbies, interests):
Education:
Career Accomplishments:
Books or Poems Published/Awards:

Listening and Speaking

Use the lines below to prepare your dramatic reading of a poem in this collection.

Where should I pause slightly? _____

_____

Where should I stop longest? _____

_____

At what lines should I show different emotions? _____

_____

Which words should I stress for effect? Where should I change volume and tone?

_____

_____

© Pearson Education, Inc., publishing as Pearson Prentice Hall. All rights reserved.

Poetry Collection: Shel Silverstein, Octavio Paz, Rachel Field
Enrichment: The Circus

Circus-type shows go back thousands of years to ancient Rome. Roman circuses featured chariot races and men standing on the backs of two horses that raced around a track. Star performers in the Roman circus were sometimes eaten by wild animals. Soldiers matched their combat skills against one another and against animals with bloody results. Later, during the Middle Ages, people performed circus-type acts on village street corners. They walked on tightropes, juggled, and performed balancing acts. Many acts included a trained bear, horse, or monkey. Sometimes performers clowned and danced to music.

The circus as we know it today began in the late 1700s with the custom of performers, both human and animal, parading through the streets before the show. In a circus parade, red and gold wagons, beautiful horses, and exotic animals make a colorful sight, while the band plays spirited music. Clowns make spectators laugh with their funny tricks. Sometimes dozens of dancers take part in the spectacle. In many cities, circus parades have been discontinued because of heavy traffic, but circuses still begin with a parade around the performing arena. Colorful sights, daring acrobatic feats, trained animals, rousing music, popcorn, peanuts, and sticky cotton candy—the modern circus is a spectacle.

A. DIRECTIONS: *Fill in the details that make the modern circus a sensory feast.*

	The Circus: A Feast for Your Five Senses
Sight	
Sound	
Smell	
Taste	
Touch	

B. DIRECTIONS: *Check off the details in the chart that apply to the circus in various periods.*

	chariot races	horses	trained animals	jugglers	tightrope walkers	parades	music	clowns	dancers
Ancient Rome									
Middle Ages									
Modern Times									

Unit 4 Resources: Poetry
© Pearson Education, Inc., publishing as Pearson Prentice Hall. All rights reserved.

Name _____ Date _____

Poetry Collection: Shel Silverstein, Octavio Paz, Rachel Field
Selection Test A

Critical Reading *Identify the letter of the choice that best answers the question.*

_____ 1. What does someone want to give the speaker in "No Thank You"?
A. a gerbil
B. a kitten
C. a baby monkey
D. a puppy

_____ 2. In "No Thank You," what is the speaker's attitude toward pets?
A. humorous
B. accepting
C. fearful
D. admiring

_____ 3. What sound device does the poet use in these lines from "No Thank You"?
I have room for mice and gerbils, / I have beds for boars and bats,
A. punctuation
B. rhymes
C. onomatopoeia
D. repetition

_____ 4. In "No Thank You," which line tells you that the speaker may be changing his or her mind?
A. No more long hair in my cornflakes,
B. I've developed allergies.
C. If you've got an ape, I'll take him,
D. Well . . . it is kind of cute at that.

_____ 5. The words in the title of "Wind and water and stone" are used throughout the poem. What sound device is this?
A. rhyme
B. onomatopoeia
C. repetition
D. punctuation

© Pearson Education, Inc., publishing as Pearson Prentice Hall. All rights reserved.

_____ 6. There is no stop or pause after one of the lines in this passage from "Wind and water and stone." After which line will you not stop or pause?

Line 1: One is the other, and is neither:
Line 2: among their empty names
Line 3: they pass and disappear,
Line 4: water and stone and wind.

A. Line 1
B. Line 2
C. Line 3
D. Line 4

_____ 7. Which pair of words best describes the speaker's attitude toward elements of nature in "Wind and water and stone"?

A. ignorant and uncaring
B. joyful and loving
C. angry and scared
D. calm and accepting

_____ 8. As you read these three lines from "Parade," where will you pause or stop?

Till leisurely and last of all
Camels and elephants will pass
Beneath our elms, along our grass.

A. after the words *all* and *pass*
B. after the words *elms* and *grass*
C. after the words *leisurely* and *last*
D. after the words *Till* and *Beneath*

_____ 9. Why does the speaker in "Parade" seem to enjoy the parade?

A. It is an unusual event.
B. Everyone is friendly for a change.
C. It happens outdoors.
D. It is free entertainment.

_____ 10. The words *blare, clashing,* and *roar* in "Parade" are examples of which sound device?

A. punctuation
B. onomatopoeia
C. alliteration
D. repetition

© Pearson Education, Inc., publishing as Pearson Prentice Hall. All rights reserved.

Vocabulary and Grammar

___ 11. Which sentence uses the underlined vocabulary word *incorrectly*?

   A. The water <u>murmurs</u> as it goes over the rocks.

   B. The kitten walked in a slow and <u>leisurely</u> way, as if it had no fear.

   C. Stamping with their boots, the children <u>dispersed</u> the water in the puddles.

   D. We rushed at a <u>leisurely</u> pace to be in the front row at the parade.

___ 12. What is the best paraphrase of the italicized idiom from "Parade"?

   Spick and span / Will shine each gilded cage and van;

   A. Neat and clean

   B. New and old

   C. Happy and shiny

   D. Gold and silver

___ 13. Which sentence uses an underlined Academic Vocabulary word *incorrectly*?

   A. Can you <u>explain</u> what Mr. Silverstein has against cats?

   B. The ideas in a poem may <u>represent</u> the poet's views.

   C. Please <u>convey</u> these lines in your best Spanish.

   D. This <u>passage</u> from "Parade" is easy to <u>paraphrase</u>.

___ 14. A *predicate noun* renames or identifies the subject of a sentence. It follows a linking verb such as a form of the verb "to be." Which sentence contains a predicate noun?

   A. The wind carved the stone.

   B. The stone is quiet.

   C. The stone stopped the wind.

   D. The stone is a cup.

Essay

15. Poets use the sound devices of repetition, alliteration, and onomatopoeia to emphasize the sounds and musical qualities of words. Choose a sound device and tell, in a brief essay, how the sound device is used in "No Thank You," "Wind and water and stone," or "Parade." You may use examples from one or more of the poems.

16. In "Parade," the poet describes what you might see and hear at a circus parade. In a brief essay, give one example that you can remember from the poem of what you might see and another example of what you might hear at a parade. Then, give two examples of your own that are not in Rachel Field's poem. Tell what you might smell and what you might taste at a parade.

© Pearson Education, Inc., publishing as Pearson Prentice Hall. All rights reserved.

Name _____ Date _____

Poetry Collection: Shel Silverstein, Octavio Paz, Rachel Field
Selection Test B

Critical Reading *Identify the letter of the choice that best completes the statement or answers the question.*

____ 1. The speaker in the poem "No Thank You" is saying no to
   A. having to say thank you.
   B. being given a kitten.
   C. being given an ape or a lion.
   D. having any kind of pet.

____ 2. In "No Thank You," the speaker's attitude toward kittens is
   A. humorous.
   B. sympathetic.
   C. fearful.
   D. admiring.

____ 3. In "No Thank You," the line "No cute, cuddly kitty-poo," contains the sound device of
   A. repetition.
   B. alliteration.
   C. onomatopoeia.
   D. punctuation.

____ 4. As you read these lines from "No Thank You," after which words would you stop longest?
   Quick—'fore it becomes a cat.
   Well . . . it is kind of cute at that.

   A. *Quick* and *Well*
   B. *cat* and *that*
   C. *'fore* and *it*
   D. *becomes* and *cute*

____ 5. What is the relationship of the three natural elements in "Wind and water and stone"?
   A. They cause problems for each other.
   B. They are all free for humans to enjoy.
   C. They act upon each other.
   D. They create each other.

____ 6. Which word from "Wind and water and stone" is an example of onomatopoeia?
   A. hollowed
   B. stone
   C. runs
   D. murmurs

_____ 7. In "Wind and water and stone," the speaker suggests that the natural elements
   A. are in danger of being eroded.
   B. shape each other.
   C. are static, or never move.
   D. stay the same shape.

_____ 8. After which word would you pause, but not stop, when reading these lines from "Wind and water and stone"?
   among their empty names
   they pass and disappear,
   water and stone and wind.

   A. names
   B. pass
   C. disappear
   D. wind

_____ 9. After which words would you pause as you read these lines from "Parade"?
   This is the day the circus comes
   With blare of brass, with beating drums,
   And clashing cymbals, and with roar
   Of wild beasts never heard before

   A. *brass, drums, cymbals*
   B. *day, and, Of*
   C. *comes, roar, before*
   D. *day, blare, beasts*

_____ 10. In "Parade," one feature that the speaker enjoys about the circus parade is
   A. the food sold by vendors.
   B. the friendliness as everyone watches.
   C. the unusual nature of the event.
   D. a chance to spend time outside.

_____ 11. Which word best describes the speaker's attitude in "Parade"?
   A. fear
   B. excitement
   C. curiosity
   D. boredom

_____ 12. Which sound device is used in the following line from "Parade"?
   Beneath our elms, along our grass.

   A. repetition
   B. alliteration
   C. onomatopoeia
   D. rhyme

____ 13. Which line from "Parade" does not use alliteration?
   A. With blare of brass, with beating drums.
   B. Within town limits. Spick and span
   C. And clashing cymbals, and with roar
   D. Till leisurely and last of all

Vocabulary and Grammar

____ 14. Which sentence uses the underlined vocabulary word *incorrectly*?
   A. A gentle breeze <u>murmurs</u> in the trees.
   B. We rushed <u>leisurely</u> to be first in line.
   C. Clouds <u>dispersed</u> as the sun came out.
   D. I can't hear him when he <u>murmurs</u>.

____ 15. What is the best paraphrase of the idiom in these lines from "Parade"?
   Spick and span
   Will shine each gilded cage and van;
   A. neat and clean
   B. showy and expensive
   C. Each cage and van is new and roomy.
   D. pulled and pushed

____ 16. Which sentence uses an underlined Academic Vocabulary word *incorrectly*?
   A. Can you <u>explain</u> the difference between a predicate adjective and a predicate noun?
   B. Two students will <u>represent</u> each point of view during the discussion.
   C. She will <u>convey</u> "Wind and water and stone" into Spanish.
   D. Please <u>paraphrase</u> this <u>passage</u> from "No Thank You."

____ 17. In which sentence is the predicate adjective underlined?
   A. The motionless stone is <u>quiet</u>.
   B. The wind sculpted the <u>stone</u>.
   C. The stone is a cup of <u>water</u>.
   D. The <u>stone</u> stopped the wind.

Essay

18. "No Thank You," "Wind and water and stone," and "Parade" use sound devices such as repetition, alliteration, and onomatopoeia. In an essay, identify a sound device found in one of the poems and explain how the poet uses the sound device in an outstanding way. Support your ideas with examples from the poem.

19. Choose one of the poems ("No Thank You," "Wind and water and stone," or "Parade"), and explain in an essay why it is important to read the poem according to its punctuation. Give an example of at least one line in which the meaning would be lost if the reader ignored the punctuation.

© Pearson Education, Inc., publishing as Pearson Prentice Hall. All rights reserved.

Vocabulary Warm-up Word Lists

Study these words from the poetry of William Shakespeare, Diana Chang, and Gwendolyn Brooks. Then, apply your knowledge to the activities that follow.

Word List A

approach [uh PROHCH] *v.* to come up to or near to
   The airplane began to <u>approach</u> the airport for landing.

charm [CHAHRM] *v.* to attract through grace, wit, or beauty
   Luis knew that he could <u>charm</u> his teachers by simply being polite.

loudness [LOWD nes] *n.* large amount of sound
   The <u>loudness</u> of the music at the concert hurt Carl's ears.

lullaby [LUHL uh by] *n.* gentle song sung to help a baby fall sleep
   Marina sang her child to sleep with a gentle <u>lullaby</u>.

melody [MEL uh dee] *n.* tune
   Alexis hummed the <u>melody</u> of her favorite song.

rather [RA<u>TH</u> uhr] *adv.* more willingly
   I would <u>rather</u> eat a peach than a banana.

Word List B

actually [AK choo uh lee] *adv.* in reality
   Tina believed that she could win the race only if she <u>actually</u> tried her hardest.

hushes [HUSH ez] *v.* makes someone be quiet
   The librarian <u>hushes</u> the noisy students.

spotted [SPAHT ed] *adj.* having small areas of skin or fur that are different in color
   Paul looked at the <u>spotted</u> leopard in the zoo.

thorny [THAWR nee] *adj.* covered in sharp points
   The children were scratched while running through the <u>thorny</u> bushes.

weaving [WEEV ing] *adj.* making a web, cloth, or a basket by passing threads or strips over and under each other
   The <u>weaving</u> spider was making a new web in the tree.

whiteness [WYT nis] *n.* the state of being white or blank
   Melissa loved the <u>whiteness</u> of the new fallen snow.

© Pearson Education, Inc., publishing as Pearson Prentice Hall. All rights reserved.

Poetry Collection: William Shakespeare, Diana Chang, and Gwendolyn Brooks
Vocabulary Warm-up Exercises

Exercise A *Fill in each blank in the paragraph below with an appropriate word from Word List A. Use each word only once.*

Kara loved to sing a [1] _____ to her baby brother every night. She would [2] _____ his crib gently, moving in closer to watch him as he relaxed. Then, she would start to sing the [3] _____ of his favorite song. She would make sure to soften the [4] _____ of her voice so as not to make too much noise.

    Kara knew she could [5] _____ her brother into smiling with the sound of her voice. When Kara saw her baby brother smile, she thought that she would [6] _____ sing to him than do anything else in the world.

Exercise B *Decide whether the following statements are true or false. Circle* T *or* F, *and then explain your answers.*

1. If an animal is <u>spotted</u>, it has one even color all over its body.
   T / F _____

2. A person must be careful when touching a <u>thorny</u> plant so as not to be scratched by small, sharp things on the plant.
   T / F _____

3. <u>Weaving</u> involves moving threads or strips together in a pattern to create something.
   T / F _____

4. If you <u>actually</u> believe something, you do not really think it is true.
   T / F _____

5. If someone <u>hushes</u> you, they are asking you to make less noise.
   T / F _____

6. <u>Whiteness</u> is a state of having many colors or being dirty.
   T / F _____

Name _____ Date _____

Read the following passage. Pay special attention to the underlined words. Then, read it again, and complete the activities. Use a separate sheet of paper for your written answers.

Jun barely knew what to think when her grandmother arrived from China. Grandma Lian had never been to America before. She didn't even speak any English. Jun had never learned Chinese. Jun was happy to see her grandmother, but it was hard to have a conversation.

The first night after she arrived, Grandma Lian came into Jun's room. She began to <u>approach</u> Jun's bed while Jun was falling asleep. As Grandma Lian moved closer, Jun wondered how she could talk to her grandmother. Soon, Grandma Lian began to sing a <u>lullaby</u> in Chinese. Though Jun didn't understand the words to this gentle song, the tune helped her fall asleep. As Grandma Lian sung, she toned down the <u>loudness</u> of her voice. Her voice got softer and softer until finally Jun drifted off to sleep.

The next morning, Jun sat down in the kitchen with her grandmother. She started to sing what she remembered of the tune from the night before. First, Jun hummed the <u>melody</u> of the song. Grandma Lian began to sing the Chinese words. Jun repeated the foreign words carefully. The sound of the strange words on her tongue delighted Jun.

When Jun's father heard his daughter singing in Chinese, he decided to join in the song. After the song was over, he translated the words to Jun. He explained the meanings of each word in the lullaby. Jun was happy to learn Chinese this way.

"I would <u>rather</u> learn Chinese from you than learn it from a book or a tape," Jun said.

Grandma Lian sat in her chair smiling. She was pleased that Jun had begun to speak Chinese. From that point on, Jun knew that she could always <u>charm</u> her grandmother by speaking to her in Chinese.

1. Underline the words that explain what it means to <u>approach</u> something. Then, use the word *approach* in a sentence.

2. Circle the words that tell you the purpose of Grandma Lian's <u>lullaby</u>. Write a sentence about your favorite childhood *lullaby*.

3. Circle the words that help you understand what <u>loudness</u> means. Then, describe *loudness* in your own words.

4. Underline the nearby word that has the same meaning as <u>melody</u>. Then, use *melody* in a sentence.

5. Underline the word that tells from whom Jun would <u>rather</u> learn than a book or tape. Then, write a sentence using *rather*.

6. Circle the words that tell how Grandma Lian felt when Jun would <u>charm</u> her by speaking Chinese. What kinds of things do you do when you want to *charm* someone?

© Pearson Education, Inc., publishing as Pearson Prentice Hall. All rights reserved.

Poetry Collection: William Shakespeare, Diana Chang, and Gwendolyn Brooks
Reading Warm-up B

Read the following passage. Pay special attention to the underlined words. Then, read it again, and complete the activities. Use a separate sheet of paper for your written answers.

In William Shakespeare's day, audiences expected a little of everything. A play had to entertain the audience; otherwise, they would walk out. When Shakespeare began to fill the whiteness of a page with ink, he also added the color of songs, dances, and special effects.

A Midsummer Night's Dream is one of Shakespeare's comedies. It takes place in a magical forest ruled by fairies. One night, humans come into the forest. They get lost and wander through tangled, thorny bushes that scratch them and tear their clothes. Then, the fairy king and queen perform some spells on the humans. None of the spells do any harm. Instead, Shakespeare uses them to make the audience laugh. For example, the king puts a spell on one character that gives him donkey ears. Then he performs another spell that makes the fairy queen fall in love with the character. She thinks the ears look *lovely,* when actually they look silly. Throughout the play, Shakespeare connects the stories of humans and fairies. By blending the stories together, he uses make-believe situations to write about themes like love and friendship.

At one point, the fairies sing "The Fairies' Lullaby." The song hushes the forest creatures into silence and tells them to stay away. In each verse, the fairies describe different creatures. Because the lullaby is a song, Shakespeare uses poetic language. For example, a spider is called "a long-legged spinner" because weaving spiders make webs. Some words are included to make the rhythm of the song work. For instance, a snake is called a spotted snake. Although some snakes are marked with spots, Shakespeare probably added the word "spotted" to put extra beats in the line.

Although the song is unimportant to the plot, it sets a mood. It also gives the audience some singing and dancing to enjoy. Shakespeare knew he had to give his audiences a little of everything.

1. Underline the word that means almost the opposite of whiteness. Then, write a sentence using the word *whiteness.*

2. Circle the words that help you know what thorny means. Would you like to touch something that is *thorny*? Explain.

3. Underline the nearby word that tells how the donkey ears actually look. Give a synonym for the word *actually*.

4. Circle the phrase that explains what hushes means. Define *hushes* in your own words.

5. Circle the words that tell you what weaving means. Then, write a sentence using the word *weaving*.

6. Underline the words that tell you what something looks like if it is spotted. What is something you know that is *spotted*?

© Pearson Education, Inc., publishing as Pearson Prentice Hall. All rights reserved.

Name _____ Date _____

Reading: Read Aloud According to Punctuation

Paraphrasing is restating something in your own words. To paraphrase a poem, you must first understand it and then use simpler language to restate its meaning. **Reading aloud according to punctuation** will help you find clues to a poem's meaning.

- When you read a poem aloud, do not automatically stop at the end of each line.
- Pause only at punctuation marks, as if you were reading a prose passage.

Even when you read poetry silently to yourself, it will make more sense if you follow these rules:

- **No punctuation** at the ends of lines: don't stop
- **After a comma (,):** slight pause
- **After a colon (:), semicolon (;), or dash (—):** longer pause
- **After endmarks—a period (.), question mark (?), or exclamation point (!):** full stop

A. DIRECTIONS: *Below are the first five lines from the poem "Cynthia in the Snow." For each line, write the letters SP for slight pause, LP for longer pause, FS for full stop, or DS for don't stop. The first line has been done for you as an example.*

Line 1: It SUSHES.   <u> FS </u>

Line 2: It hushes   <u>   </u>

Line 3: The loudness in the road.   <u>   </u>

Line 4: It flitter-twitters,   <u>   </u>

Line 5: And laughs away from me.   <u>   </u>

B. DIRECTIONS: *Briefly explain why a good reader will not pause between lines 2 and 3.*

_____

_____

_____

_____

_____

_____

_____

_____

_____

_____

© Pearson Education, Inc., publishing as Pearson Prentice Hall. All rights reserved.

Name _____ Date _____

Poetry Collection: William Shakespeare, Diana Chang, Gwendolyn Brooks
Literary Analysis: Sound Devices

Sound devices are a writer's tools for bringing out the music in words and for expressing feelings. Sound devices commonly used in poetry include the following:

- **Repetition:** the use, more than once, of any element of language—a sound, word, phrase, clause, or sentence—as in *This land is your land/ This land is my land*
- **Alliteration:** the repetition of initial consonant sounds, such as the *b* sound in *beautiful big brown eyes* or the *cl* sound in *clattered* and *clashed*
- **Onomatopoeia:** the use of a word that sounds like what it means, such as *patter* and *roar*

A. DIRECTIONS: *Underline the repetition, alliteration, and onomatopoeia in the following lines from the poetry collection. On the line after each item, write R for repetition, A for alliteration, and O for onomatopoeia. Some items will have more than one letter. The first one has been done for you.*

1. You <u>spotted snakes</u> with double tongue   _____A_____
2. Lulla, lulla, lullaby, lulla, lulla lullaby   _____
3. "Are you Chinese?"/"Yes." /"American?"/"Yes"   _____
4. Not neither-nor/not maybe   _____
5. It SUSHES   _____
6. And whitely whirs away   _____

B. DIRECTIONS: *Find one example of repetition, one example of alliteration, and one example of onomatopoeia in this passage. Then, write the examples on the lines below.*

There would be no stargazing, no night hike, and no campfire until the weather cleared. We scrambled into our sleeping bags, determined to get some rest. The drip, drip, drip of the rain on the roof of the tent finally put us to sleep. We woke up suddenly when we heard Roy shouting outside. We unzipped the tent and saw a big, brown bear standing on its hind legs at the edge of the woods. We grabbed pans and banged on them as the bear crashed through the bushes to escape the noise.

1. Example of repetition: _____
2. Example of alliteration: _____
3. Example of onomatopoeia: _____

Poetry Collection: William Shakespeare, Diana Chang, Gwendolyn Brooks
Vocabulary Builder

Word List

nigh	offense

A. DIRECTIONS: *Think about the meaning of the italicized word in each item and answer the question.*

1. If you spend the night at a friend's house talking all night, and now morning is *nigh*, how do feel? Tell why.

   _____

   _____

2. What traffic *offense* is likely to get a driver into trouble?

   _____

   _____

B. DIRECTIONS: *Following the instructions, use each Word List word correctly.*

1. Use *nigh* in a sentence about a storm that is about to arrive.

   _____

   _____

2. Use *offense* in a sentence about a misunderstanding.

   _____

   _____

C. DIRECTIONS: *Write the letter of the word that means the* opposite *of the word in* CAPITAL LETTERS.

___ 1. NIGH
      A. close   **B.** near   **C.** far   **D.** yes

___ 2. OFFENSE
      A. guilt   **B.** kindness   **C.** crime   **D.** harm

© Pearson Education, Inc., publishing as Pearson Prentice Hall. All rights reserved.

Poetry Collection: William Shakespeare, Diana Chang, Gwendolyn Brooks
Support for Writing a Prose Description

Use the chart to create your list of details for your prose description of the picture that the poet painted. This list will help you focus on details that appeal to the senses.

Details I Might See:
Details I Might Smell:
Details I Might Hear:
Details I Might Touch or Be Able to Feel:
Details I Might Taste:

Now, use the details you have collected to write your prose description.

© Pearson Education, Inc., publishing as Pearson Prentice Hall. All rights reserved.

Poetry Collection: William Shakespeare, Diana Chang, Gwendolyn Brooks
Support for Extend Your Learning

Research and Technology

Use the chart to record the facts for the résumé of the poet you have chosen.

Name of Poet: _____

Personal Information (birthplace, childhood, family, travel, hobbies, interests):
Education:
Career:
Books or Poems Published/Awards:

Listening and Speaking

Use the lines below to prepare your dramatic reading of a poem in this collection.

Where should I pause slightly? _____

_____

Where should I stop longest? _____

_____

At what lines should I show different emotions? _____

_____

Which words should I stress for effect? Where should I change volume and tone?

_____

_____

© Pearson Education, Inc., publishing as Pearson Prentice Hall. All rights reserved.

Poetry Collection: William Shakespeare, Diana Chang, Gwendolyn Brooks
Enrichment: Nature and Nurture

Diana Chang suggests in her poem that we are who we are because we are born that way. Some people agree with her. Others say that our experiences and the way we remember them shape us into the people we are. Many scientists believe that both views are correct; they call this **nature and nurture**. By nature, we are born with certain traits and abilities, such as shyness, impatience, or athletic or musical ability. Our experiences nurture, or affect, those traits. Research has shown that personality continues to change as a result of new experiences and changes in the environment.

Not all scientists agree on the nature-and-nurture theory. Some believe that the personality traits we are born with determine our behavior. Others believe that what people do, think, and feel depend on the conditions in which their behavior occurs. For example, people may be honest in one situation and dishonest in another.

Experts agree that we cannot completely change the traits we are born with, but we can change the way we act.

DIRECTIONS: *Write your answers to the following questions on the lines provided.*

1. **A.** What traits do you admire in others?

   _____

   _____

   _____

   B. What actions could you take to help you strengthen these traits in yourself?

   _____

   _____

   _____

2. How could someone change his or her actions to overcome each of the following traits?

   Shyness: _____

   _____

   _____

   Laziness: _____

   _____

   _____

3. Imagine that your friend has a quick temper. This often leads to trouble for your friend and others. How do you think he or she could change this trait?

   _____

   _____

© Pearson Education, Inc., publishing as Pearson Prentice Hall. All rights reserved.

Poetry Collections: Shel Silverstein, Octavio Paz, Rachel Field;
William Shakespeare, Diana Chang, Gwendolyn Brooks

Build Language Skills: Vocabulary

Idioms

Paraphrasing idioms helps you understand a text. When you paraphrase an idiom, you restate it in a way that tells what it means.

    The coach was willing to *go to bat* for us.

    The coach was willing to *defend* us.

A. PRACTICE: *Paraphrase each italicized idiom by restating it on the line below.*

1. What should you do when a friend *gives you the cold shoulder* at school?

    _____

2. The terrier puppy we got from the pound *is a diamond in the rough.*

    _____

3. My sister wanted to try out for the lead in the school musical, but she *got cold feet.*

    _____

4. Sonya is *in hot water* because she didn't call home to say she would be late.

    _____

Academic Vocabulary Practice

convey	explain	paraphrase	passage	represent

B. DIRECTIONS: *Following the instructions, use each Academic Vocabulary word correctly.*

1. Use *convey* in a sentence about a message you hope to make in a speech. _____

    _____

2. Use *explain* in a question about something you would like to understand. _____

    _____

3. Use *paraphrase* in a sentence about a homework assignment. _____

    _____

4. Use *passage* in a sentence about a favorite part of a book you have read. _____

    _____

5. Use *represent* in a sentence about the student council. _____

    _____

© Pearson Education, Inc., publishing as Pearson Prentice Hall. All rights reserved.

Name _____ Date _____

Build Language Skills: Grammar

Predicate Nouns and Predicate Adjectives

Some sentences use linking verbs such as *be, is, were, feel, appear,* or *seems*. In those sentences, the **subject complements** that complete the idea of the subject and verb are called predicate nouns or predicate adjectives. A **predicate noun** renames or identifies the subject of a sentence. A **predicate adjective** describes the subject of a sentence.

> Octavio Paz was a Mexican poet. (predicate noun—*identifies* the subject, Octavio Paz)
> His poems seem timeless. (predicate adjective—*describes* poems)

A. PRACTICE: *Look at the underlined subject complement in each sentence. Draw an arrow to the word or phrase that the subject complement renames or describes. Then, write whether the subject complement is a predicate noun or a predicate adjective. The first one has been done for you.*

1. The sky was cloudy all day. predicate adjective

2. William Shakespeare's plays are famous all over the world.

3. Sacramento is the capital of California.

4. Kira and Naomi were the highest scorers in the game.

5. A sari is the traditional outer garment of a Hindu woman.

6. Commercials on television are often loud and annoying.

B. WRITING APPLICATION: *Write five sentences to describe a place in nature that you have seen. Use predicate nouns or predicate adjectives in your sentences. Underline and number five predicate nouns and predicate adjectives. Then, write PN or PA next to the item number below your description.*

1. _____

2. _____

3. _____

4. _____

5. _____

1. _____   2. _____   3. _____   4. _____   5. _____

© Pearson Education, Inc., publishing as Pearson Prentice Hall. All rights reserved.

Poetry Collection: William Shakespeare, Diana Chang, Gwendolyn Brooks
Selection Test A

Critical Reading *Identify the letter of the choice that best answers the question.*

_____ 1. Why are the fairies singing a lullaby?
   A. to put their queen to sleep
   B. to put their babies to sleep
   C. to put the birds to sleep
   D. to show how well they sing

_____ 2. In "The Fairies' Lullaby," what do the fairies ask the creepy insects and animals to do?
   A. eat with them
   B. entertain
   C. sing the chorus
   D. stay away

_____ 3. In "The Fairies' Lullaby," which choice is an example of alliteration?
   A. sweet lullaby
   B. spotted snakes
   C. Weaving spiders
   D. Worm nor snail

_____ 4. When you read these three lines from "The Fairies' Lullaby," after which word would you continue reading, without pausing or stopping?
      Philomel, with melody
      Sing in our sweet lullaby;
      Lulla, lulla, lullaby, lulla, lulla, lullaby.
   A. Philomel
   B. melody
   C. lullaby
   D. lulla

_____ 5. When the poet uses the word *yes* four times in "Saying Yes," which sound device is she using?
   A. alliteration
   B. onomatopoeia
   C. repetition
   D. punctuation

© Pearson Education, Inc., publishing as Pearson Prentice Hall. All rights reserved.

_____ 6. In "Saying Yes," what does the repetition of the word "*Really*" suggest about the questioner?

A. The questioner does not believe the speaker's answers.

B. It is the questioner who is the real American.

C. The questioner cannot hear the speaker's soft answers.

D. The questioner knows he or she is annoying the speaker.

_____ 7. In "Saying Yes," what does the speaker consider herself to be?

A. mostly American

B. mostly Chinese

C. both Chinese and American

D. neither Chinese nor American

_____ 8. Which choice is the correct way to read this line?

It SUSHES.

A. Pause slightly at the end of the line.

B. Stop completely before going on to the next line.

C. Keep going without pausing.

D. Pause between the word *It* and the word *SUSHES*.

_____ 9. In "Cynthia in the Snow," what sound device was used when the poet wrote the word *SUSHES*?

A. symbolism

B. repetition

C. alliteration

D. onomatopoeia

_____ 10. In "Cynthia in the Snow," how does Cynthia feel about the snow?

A. lonely, scared

B. hurt, sad

C. delighted, surprised

D. playful, awe-struck

_____ 11. What does this line in "Cynthia in the Snow" mean?

It hushes
The loudness in the road.

A. The snow tells the road to be quiet.

B. The snow muffles the sound of passing cars.

C. The snow causes accidents that close the road.

D. The snow is singing a lullaby to the cars.

© Pearson Education, Inc., publishing as Pearson Prentice Hall. All rights reserved.

Vocabulary and Grammar

_____ 12. Which sentence uses the underlined vocabulary word *incorrectly?*

A. Her <u>offense</u> was minor, but she was suspended from school because of it.

B. Driving through a red light is a serious traffic <u>offense</u>.

C. It gets dark when day changes to <u>nigh</u>.

D. We were glad to hear that the cabin was <u>nigh</u>.

_____ 13. Choose the best paraphrase of the italicized idiom in this sentence:

The queen *caught some Zs* while the fairies protected her from harm.

A. trapped enemies

B. worked hard

C. played a game

D. slept

_____ 14. Which Academic Vocabulary word best completes this sentence?

Out of love and respect, in any debate about her rights and privileges, the fairies in "The Fairies' Lullaby" would be most likely to _____ their queen.

A. convey

B. explain

C. paraphrase

D. represent

_____ 15. Which sentence contains a predicate adjective?

A. You are Chinese.

B. These are spotted snakes.

C. Sing in our sweet lullaby.

D. It hushes the loudness in the road.

Essay

16. Tell which of the three poems—"The Fairies' Lullaby," "Saying Yes," or "Cynthia in the Snow"—you like best. Give two reasons why you like it. Support each reason with at least one example from the poem.

17. Choose one of the poems—"The Fairies' Lullaby," "Saying Yes," or "Cynthia in the Snow." In an essay, explain how one sound device—repetition, alliteration, or onomatopoeia—gives the poem a musical effect or contributes to your understanding of what the poet is saying.

© Pearson Education, Inc., publishing as Pearson Prentice Hall. All rights reserved.

Poetry Collection: William Shakespeare, Diana Chang, Gwendolyn Brooks
Selection Test B

Critical Reading *Identify the letter of the choice that best completes the statement or answers the question.*

_____ 1. In "The Fairies' Lullaby," the fairies ask the insects and animals to
    A. eat with them.
    B. sing with them.
    C. stay away.
    D. entertain.

_____ 2. In "The Fairies' Lullaby," the creatures that the fairies speak to are
    A. kind.
    B. creepy.
    C. magical.
    D. powerful.

_____ 3. The phrase "spotted snakes" in "The Fairies' Lullaby" is an example of
    A. alliteration.
    B. punctuation.
    C. repetition.
    D. onomatopoeia.

_____ 4. When you read these two lines from "The Fairies' Lullaby," after which words would you pause?
    Philomel, with melody
    Sing in our sweet lullaby;
    A. *with* and *sweet*
    B. *melody* and *lullaby*
    C. *melody* and *Sing*
    D. *Philomel* and *lullaby*

_____ 5. In "The Fairies' Lullaby," the seven lines that are repeated are said by
    A. the fairies.
    B. the queen.
    C. the Chorus.
    D. Philomel.

_____ 6. In which passage from "Saying Yes" does the poet uses the sound device of repetition?
    A. But I would rather say / yes,
    B. "*Really* Chinese?" / "No . . . not quite." / "*Really* American?"
    C. The homes I've had, / the ways I am
    D. I'd rather say it / twice

© Pearson Education, Inc., publishing as Pearson Prentice Hall. All rights reserved.

Name _____ Date _____

____ **7.** In "Saying Yes," the questioner's use of the word "*Really*" suggests that
   A. the questioner may not believe the speaker's answers.
   B. the questioner is really an American.
   C. the speaker is answering so softly that it is hard to hear her answers.
   D. the speaker is refusing to answer the question.

____ **8.** In "Saying Yes," when the speaker says, "I'd rather say it twice," she means she would rather
   A. emphasize that she is Chinese.
   B. emphasize that she is American.
   C. tell her questioner to leave her alone.
   D. say she is both Chinese and American.

____ **9.** When reading "Saying Yes," after which word in these lines would you *not* pause?
   But I would rather say
   yes.
   Not neither-nor,
   not maybe,

   A. say
   B. yes
   C. neither-nor
   D. maybe

____ **10.** Which choice is the correct way to read this first line of "Cynthia in the Snow"?
   It SUSHES.

   A. Pause slightly at the end of the line.
   B. Stop completely at the end of the line.
   C. Keep going without pausing at the end of the line.
   D. Pause between the word *It* and the word *SUSHES*.

____ **11.** In "Cynthia in the Snow," what do these lines about the snow mean?
   It hushes / The loudness in the road.

   A. The snow tells the road to be quiet.
   B. The snow is singing a lullaby.
   C. Car noises drown out all other sounds.
   D. The snow muffles the sounds of cars.

____ **12.** In "Cynthia in the Snow," the word *hushes* is an example of
   A. symbolism.
   B. repetition.
   C. alliteration.
   D. onomatopoeia.

© Pearson Education, Inc., publishing as Pearson Prentice Hall. All rights reserved.

_____ 13. In "Cynthia in the Snow," the snow "laughs away from me." Who is "me"?
   A. the speaker in the poem
   B. a snowflake
   C. a car driver
   D. Cynthia's mother

_____ 14. In "Cynthia in the Snow," the speaker's overall reaction to the snow is best described as
   A. sad.
   B. hurt.
   C. delighted.
   D. suspicious.

Vocabulary and Grammar

_____ 15. Which sentence uses the underlined vocabulary word *incorrectly*?
   A. A snail commits an <u>offense</u> when it eats the flowers I have planted.
   B. The snail deserves a reward for each <u>offense</u> it commits.
   C. When morning is <u>nigh</u>, the night creatures leave the garden.
   D. From the coldness in the air, we knew that a snowstorm was <u>nigh</u>.

_____ 16. Choose the best paraphrase of this idiom: "Their queen was the apple of the fairies' eye."
   A. The queen loved fairies and apples.
   B. The queen made apples grow.
   C. The queen loved the fairies' apples.
   D. The fairies loved their queen.

_____ 17. Which sentence uses the underlined academic vocabulary word *incorrectly*?
   A. The fairies <u>represent</u> the best interests of their queen.
   B. Can you <u>explain</u> Diana Chang's outlook on her identity in "Saying Yes"?
   C. Gwendolyn Brooks describes Cynthia's <u>passage</u> in "Cynthia in the Snow."
   D. A paraphrase of "The Fairies' Lullaby" should <u>convey</u> a description of the scene.

_____ 18. In which sentence is the predicate noun underlined?
   A. The snow is a lovely <u>whiteness</u>.
   B. It hushes the loudness in the <u>road</u>.
   C. It hushes the <u>loudness</u> in the road.
   D. It is so <u>beautiful</u> it hurts.

Essay

19. The authors of "The Fairies' Lullaby," "Saying Yes," and "Cynthia in the Snow" all use one or more sound devices. In an essay, compare the use of repetition, alliteration, and onomatopoeia in two of the poems. Include at least one example from each of the two poems you choose to compare.

20. In an essay, tell how "The Fairies' Lullaby" is both different from and similar to other lullabies. What would you change in "The Fairies' Lullaby" to make its content more modern?

© Pearson Education, Inc., publishing as Pearson Prentice Hall. All rights reserved.

Vocabulary Warm-up Word Lists

Study these words from the poetry of Alice Walker and Naomi Shihab Nye. Then, apply your knowledge to the activities that follow.

Word List A

circled [SER kuhld] *v.* traveled around the outside of something in a circle
The bee <u>circled</u> the flower before landing upon the petal.

forgotten [fawr GAHT en] *v.* not remembered
Ernesto had <u>forgotten</u> to bring his textbook to class.

infinite [IN fuh nit] *adj.* endless
The sky is <u>infinite</u> and stretches on forever.

naïve [nye EEV] *adj.* not experienced
Roberta was <u>naïve</u> about how to manage her money.

neighborhood [NAY buhr hood] *n.* a small area or section of a community
Josh walked around the block, looking at the houses in his <u>neighborhood</u>.

rusted [RUHST ed] *adj.* covered with reddish brown rust, which forms when water gets on iron and steel
The metal chair became <u>rusted</u> after it was left out in the rain.

Word List B

completed [kuhm PLEE tid] *v.* finished
Roger <u>completed</u> his exam and turned it in to his teacher.

delicious [di LISH uhs] *adj.* very pleasing in taste or smell
Nick thought that the freshly picked orange was the most <u>delicious</u> fruit he had ever tasted.

delight [di LYT] *n.* great pleasure
Annabelle found <u>delight</u> in walking barefoot on the grass.

refreshing [ri FRESH ing] *adj.* making one feel fresh or strong again
Victor felt better on that hot summer day after he took a <u>refreshing</u> swim in the lake.

savoring [SAY vuhr ing] *v.* slowly enjoying; tasting with pleasure
Brenda was <u>savoring</u> every bite of food of her plate.

sweetness [SWEET nis] *n.* the state of being sweet
Marco enjoyed the sugary <u>sweetness</u> of the ice cream.

© Pearson Education, Inc., publishing as Pearson Prentice Hall. All rights reserved.

Poetry by Alice Walker and Naomi Shihab Nye
Vocabulary Warm-up Exercises

Exercise A *Fill in each blank in the paragraph below with an appropriate word from Word List A. Use each word only once.*

Richard was excited to build a new swing set. He looked at the dirty,

[1] _____ metal of his old set. Then he looked at the kit for his new one.

He [2] _____ the new kit, walking around the pile of new parts. In his

excitement, he had [3] _____ that this was not going to be an easy job.

Richard was [4] _____ and inexperienced when it came to building

things. He read the instructions for the kit. They seemed [5] _____, as

if they went on forever.

Richard worked hard to put the kit together. Then he invited all the kids who lived

in his part of town to come play at his house. He now had the best swing set in the

[6] _____.

Exercise B *Answer the questions with complete explanations.*

1. If someone gives you a piece of fruit and says it is <u>delicious</u>, would you want to eat it?

   _____

2. Would you feel satisfied after you had <u>completed</u> a difficult task?

   _____

3. How does a <u>refreshing</u> drink of water make a person feel?

   _____

4. If a person is <u>savoring</u> the flavor a new type of food, will he or she want to eat that type of food again?

   _____

5. How might a cook add <u>sweetness</u> to a dessert?

   _____

6. When you take <u>delight</u> in something, are you happy that you have experienced it?

   _____

© Pearson Education, Inc., publishing as Pearson Prentice Hall. All rights reserved.

Name _____ Date _____

Poetry by Alice Walker and Naomi Shihab Nye
Reading Warm-up A

Read the following passage. Pay special attention to the underlined words. Then, read it again, and complete the activities. Use a separate sheet of paper for your written answers.

Miguel liked to go exploring around his <u>neighborhood</u>. He never tired of looking for new things to see in his part of town. One of Miguel's favorite spots was the road behind his school. He remembered when Mr. Ramirez lived on the road before the old man went to live with his daughter. His house had stayed empty ever since.

One afternoon, Miguel went to look at the house. He <u>circled</u> the building, walking around the outside of it. The metal chairs on the back porch were <u>rusted</u> from being outside in the rain and wind. It seemed like everyone had <u>forgotten</u> about the house except for him. Certainly, no one remembered to take care of it.

Suddenly, Miguel noticed that the back door was open. He heard voices coming from inside. Miguel felt scared. A <u>naïve</u> person might think nothing was unusual. Miguel used his own common sense and experience, though. He realized that no one had a reason to be in that building.

As Miguel stood there wondering what he should do, someone spoke behind him. Miguel turned around fast. Standing behind him was a boy his own age.

"Hi," said the boy. "I'm Manny. I'm moving into my grandfather's house over there. Do you want to come in and take a look?"

Together, the boys walked into the house. Everything looked the same as it had when Mr. Ramirez lived there. The only difference was that now, all the furniture was covered in an endless, almost <u>infinite</u> amount of dust.

Manny's mother came into the room. "It looks as if Manny has made a new friend! I hope you will stick around to help us clean up all of this dust!"

Miguel smiled. He could feel the new life in the house already.

1. Underline the words that explain what a <u>neighborhood</u> is. Then, write a sentence about the *neighborhood* you live in.

2. Underline the words that tell you how Miguel <u>circled</u> the building. Then, write a sentence using *circled*.

3. Circle the words that tell you how the metal chairs became <u>rusted</u>. Then, explain what *rusted* means in your own words.

4. Underline the nearby word that has the *opposite* meaning of <u>forgotten</u>. Write a sentence of your own using *forgotten*.

5. Underline the words that tell why Miguel is not <u>naïve</u>. Then, write a sentence using *naïve*.

6. Circle the nearby word that has the same meaning as <u>infinite</u>. Describe something that you think of as *infinite*.

© Pearson Education, Inc., publishing as Pearson Prentice Hall. All rights reserved.

Name _____   Date _____

Poetry by Alice Walker and Naomi Shihab Nye
Reading Warm-up B

Read the following passage. Pay special attention to the underlined words. Then, read it again, and complete the activities. Use a separate sheet of paper for your written answers.

When was the last time you ate a <u>refreshing</u> piece of fruit? Did <u>savoring</u> it make you feel strong and fresh again? Plants create fruit specifically to be eaten by animals like you. Fruit is designed by nature to taste <u>delicious</u>. A fruit that tastes and smells pleasant is more likely to be eaten. This helps the plant spread its seeds.

Plants reproduce by creating seeds. A fruit is the part of a plant that carries seeds. An animal that eats fruit carries these seeds to faraway locations. When new plants grow out of the seeds, the plant has <u>completed</u>, or finished, its task of reproducing. Then the life cycle starts all over again.

The spreading of seeds is a vital part of the life cycle of a plant. For a plant species to survive, animals need to enjoy its fruit. The plant gives a large amount of its nutritional resources to make sure that animals do. A plant that creates fruit will store its natural sugars in the fruit. A fruit that is full of this <u>sweetness</u> is ripe and ready to be eaten.

Different types of fruit have different types of seeds. A peach, for example, has one large seed, or pit, in its center. Oranges, on the other hand, have many small seeds throughout their flesh. These varieties of seeds are designed to travel far from the trees on which they grow.

Next time you eat a piece of fruit, think about planting its seeds in the ground. Then take <u>delight</u> in the fact that you are helping to spread the seeds of the parent plant. This pleasure will surely add to your enjoyment of fruit.

1. Underline the words that tell you the meaning of <u>refreshing</u>. What is something that you find *refreshing?*

2. Underline the word that means almost the same thing as <u>savoring</u>. What is something you enjoy *savoring?*

3. Circle the sentence that explains why fruit is <u>delicious</u>. Define *delicious* in your own words.

4. Underline the nearby word with the same meaning as <u>completed</u>. Then, write a sentence using the word *completed.*

5. Circle the words that explain what gives fruit its <u>sweetness</u>. Then, define *sweetness* in your own words.

6. Underline the nearby word with a meaning similar to <u>delight</u>. Then, write a sentence using the word *delight.*

© Pearson Education, Inc., publishing as Pearson Prentice Hall. All rights reserved.

Name _____ Date _____

Name _____ Date _____

Poetry by Alice Walker and Naomi Shihab Nye
Literary Analysis: Sensory Language

In literature, **sensory language** is writing that appeals to one or more of the five senses—sight, hearing, touch, taste, and smell. The use of sensory language creates clear word pictures, or **images,** for the reader. Look at these lines of poetry, for example.

Crickets sing, curtains stir; / from the dog a gentle snore.

Soft sheets, white moon; / Summer night is at my door.

The language in this word picture appeals to several senses. The crickets' song and the dog's snore appeal to the sense of hearing. The swaying curtains and white moon appeal to the sense of sight. The soft sheets appeal to the sense of touch. All together, these images bring a summer evening to life in the reader's mind.

A. DIRECTIONS: *Read each passage. Underline words or phrases that appeal to one or more of the five senses. Then, on the lines to the right, write the senses to which each word or phrase appeals. (You do not need to write on every line.)*

from "At First, It is True, I Thought There Were Only Peaches & Wild Grapes" by Alice Walker

1. There is such _____

   A creature _____

   As the wavy green _____

   Cherimoya _____

   The black loudsmelling _____

   & delicious _____

   Durian _____

   The fleshy orange mango _____

   And the spiky, whitehearted _____

   Soursop. _____

from "Alphabet" by Naomi Shihab Nye

2. One by one _____

   the old people _____

   of our neighborhood _____

   are going up _____

   into the air _____

   their yards _____

   still wear _____

   small white narcissus _____

   sweetening winter _____

© Pearson Education, Inc., publishing as Pearson Prentice Hall. All rights reserved.

183

Poetry by Alice Walker and Naomi Shihab Nye
Vocabulary Builder

Word List

glisten	naïve	phrasings	savoring	sole

A. DIRECTIONS: *On each line, write the letter of the phrase that could be substituted for the italicized word in each sentence.*

1. ___ I am the *sole* owner of the house.
2. ___ She is still young and *naïve*.
3. ___ I am *savoring* this piece of pizza.
4. ___ The rain did *glisten* on the sidewalk.
5. ___ Each language has its own *phrasings*.

A. tasting with pleasure
B. ways of speaking
C. one and only
D. not worldly
E. shine or sparkle

B. DIRECTIONS: *Decide whether each statement below is true or false. Explain your answers.*

1. While *savoring* a meal, a person might ask for seconds.

_____

_____

2. There can be two or three *sole* winners of a contest.

_____

_____

3. You can string *phrasings* together to make a necklace.

_____

_____

4. Melting icicles *glisten* in the sunlight.

_____

_____

5. *Naïve* people believe everything that is told to them.

_____

_____

© Pearson Education, Inc., publishing as Pearson Prentice Hall. All rights reserved.

Name _____   Date _____

Poetry by Alice Walker and Naomi Shihab Nye
Support for Writing a Comparative Essay

Before you draft your essay comparing and contrasting the use of sensory language in these poems, complete the graphic organizers below. In the boxes, write examples of vivid images from each poem. Then, write down an idea that these images help the poet express.

"At First, It Is True . . ."

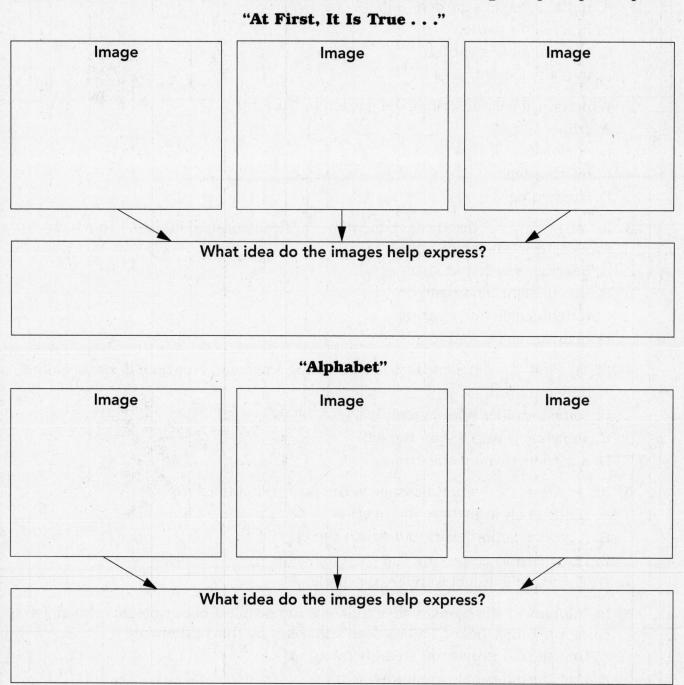

Now, use your notes to write an essay comparing and contrasting the use of sensory language in the two poems. Be sure to tell which poem you believe uses stronger, more vivid sensory language.

© Pearson Education, Inc., publishing as Pearson Prentice Hall. All rights reserved.

Poetry by Alice Walker and Naomi Shihab Nye
Selection Test A

Critical Reading *Identify the letter of the choice that best answers the question.*

_____ 1. Where does "At First . . ." take place?
   A. in the speaker's garden
   B. in a child's garden
   C. in a neighbor's garden
   D. in a city garden

_____ 2. Which word best describes the garden in "At First . . ."?
   A. empty
   B. enclosed
   C. overflowing
   D. frightening

_____ 3. In "At First . . . ," the speaker mentions a "fleshy orange mango." To which senses does this image appeal?
   A. hearing, smell, and sight
   B. touch, sight, and taste
   C. touch, smell, and hearing
   D. hearing, sight, and touch

_____ 4. In "At First . . . ," the speaker is addressing someone. To whom is she speaking?
   A. only to herself
   B. someone older than herself
   C. someone younger than herself
   D. a gardener whom she knows

_____ 5. In "At First . . . ," what message is the poet trying to express?
   A. Home is always where the heart is.
   B. A garden is hard work but worth the effort.
   C. Peaches and grapes are the most delicious fruits.
   D. The world is full of wonderful experiences.

_____ 6. In "Alphabet," the speaker says that "the old people / of our neighborhood / are going up / into the air." What does she mean by this statement?
   A. that the old people are steadily dying
   B. that the old people are taking trips
   C. that the old people are forgetting things
   D. that the old people are watching the sky

© Pearson Education, Inc., publishing as Pearson Prentice Hall. All rights reserved.

___ 7. In "Alphabet," the speaker notices small white flowers, a bare peach tree, and empty lawn chairs. To what sense do these images appeal?
A. smell
B. sight
C. taste
D. touch

___ 8. Based on the information in "Alphabet," which is probably true?
A. The speaker has very few friends.
B. The speaker is planning to move away.
C. The speaker is new to the neighborhood.
D. The speaker knows many of her neighbors.

___ 9. Which word best describes the speaker's feelings in "Alphabet"?
A. shy
B. cheerful
C. sad
D. relieved

___ 10. With what image does "Alphabet" end?
A. a tiny rooftop
B. an empty chair
C. a string of names
D. the sky above

___ 11. What message do both "At First . . ." and "Alphabet" send the reader?
A. Set goals.
B. Avoid travel.
C. Appreciate life.
D. Stay young.

___ 12. In literature, what is an image?
A. a strong sound
B. a word picture
C. something that is not real
D. one of the five senses

© Pearson Education, Inc., publishing as Pearson Prentice Hall. All rights reserved.

Vocabulary

___ 13. If a peach tree is the *sole* plant in your garden, what is it?

    A. the only plant in the garden

    B. the best plant in the garden

    C. the oldest plant in the garden

    D. one of many plants in the garden

___ 14. What does *glisten* mean in this phrase from "Alphabet"?

    . . . their stones / glisten / under the sun . . . .

    A. dry off

    B. grow warm

    C. relax

    D. sparkle

Essay

15. Each of these poems could be thought of as a list. In an essay, explain the kinds of things that are listed in each poem. In your opinion, why does each poet create such a list? What message does the list send to the reader? Use at least two details from each poem to support your explanation.

16. Poets often use language that appeals to the five senses—sight, hearing, taste, touch, and smell. In a brief essay, choose *one* sense from each poem that the poem emphasizes most strongly. Why do you think the poet chose to focus on this sense? Give at least two examples from the poems to support your ideas.

© Pearson Education, Inc., publishing as Pearson Prentice Hall. All rights reserved.

Name _____ Date _____

Poetry by Alice Walker and Naomi Shihab Nye
Selection Test B

Critical Reading *Identify the letter of the choice that best completes the statement or answers the question.*

_____ 1. The speaker of "At First . . ." says that she has been "Born / Into a garden." How does the speaker feel about this garden?
    A. uncertain
    B. delighted
    C. afraid
    D. surprised

_____ 2. In "At First . . .," the speaker mentions a "spiky, whitehearted / Soursop." To what sense does this image *not* appeal?
    A. hearing
    B. touch
    C. sight
    D. taste

_____ 3. What has the speaker of "At First . . ." come to realize about the person she used to be?
    A. She realizes she was picky.
    B. She realizes she was limited.
    C. She realizes she was hasty.
    D. She realizes she was dull.

_____ 4. What does the speaker of "At First . . ." mean when she says "I am everywhere / At home"?
    A. that she is truly happy only at home
    B. that she is not in one specific place
    C. that the entire world is her home
    D. that she would rather wander than stay put

_____ 5. In "Alphabet," what is happening in the speaker's neighborhood?
    A. The older people are moving away.
    B. Nobody is taking care of the older people.
    C. The speaker is visiting the older people.
    D. The older people are steadily dying.

_____ 6. What can you tell about the speaker from reading "Alphabet"?
    A. She has lived in her neighborhood for a long time.
    B. She does not often like to travel in airplanes.
    C. She is glad that her neighborhood is changing.
    D. She has difficulty remembering people's names.

_____ 7. Which image from "Alphabet" appeals to the sense of smell or taste?
    A. small white narcissus / sweetening winter
    B. their stones / glisten / under the sun
    C. what stood / in that brushy spot / years ago
    D. circled high above our street

© Pearson Education, Inc., publishing as Pearson Prentice Hall. All rights reserved.

_____ 8. In "Alphabet," what is the speaker most likely doing?
  A. visiting an elderly neighbor
  B. walking in her neighborhood
  C. working in her garden
  D. looking up into the sky

_____ 9. In "Alphabet," what most saddens the speaker?
  A. that there will be no more cupcakes
  B. that gardens will be neglected
  C. that so much will be forgotten
  D. that she will leave her neighborhood

_____ 10. To what sense does this image from "Alphabet" appeal?

   . . . or the time my plane / circled high above our street / the roof of our house / dotting the tiniest / "i"

  A. hearing
  B. taste
  C. touch
  D. sight

_____ 11. The speaker of "At First . . ." sees herself "Spread out / To cover / The earth." By comparison, how does the speaker of "Alphabet" see herself?
  A. She sees herself as someone who is much smaller.
  B. She sees herself as someone who is equally vast.
  C. She sees herself as someone who is even more vast.
  D. She sees herself as someone who is not in existence.

_____ 12. In literature, what is sensory language?
  A. writing that creates word pictures for the reader
  B. words that have more than one meaning
  C. writing that captures the sound of spoken language
  D. a word or a phrase that does not make sense

_____ 13. With which statement would the speakers of both "At First . . ." and "Alphabet" most likely agree?
  A. Nature is cruel.
  B. Life is precious.
  C. It is better to be young than old.
  D. Travel should be avoided.

_____ 14. If "Alphabet" is about losing, what is "At First . . ." mostly about?
  A. winning
  B. holding on
  C. discovering
  D. remembering

© Pearson Education, Inc., publishing as Pearson Prentice Hall. All rights reserved.

Vocabulary

____ **15.** When the speaker of "Alphabet" thinks of her neighbors' "formal *phrasings*," what is she thinking of?
   A. their backyards
   B. how they dressed
   C. how they spoke
   D. their furniture

____ **16.** What does the word *sole* mean in this passage from "At First . . ."?

   At first I thought / I could live / On blue plums / That fresh yellow pears / Might become / My sole delight.

   A. greatest
   B. daily
   C. simple
   D. only

____ **17.** When the speaker of "At First . . ." says "I was *naïve*, Child," what is she is saying about how she used to be?
   A. She was selfish and small-minded.
   B. There was much for her to learn.
   C. She had everything she needed.
   D. There were difficulties in her way.

Essay

18. One of the poems in this pair includes more images that appeal to sight, while the other includes more images that appeal to taste and touch. In a brief essay, identify which poem contains each kind of imagery. Then use at least two details from each poem to explain why the poems' images are well-suited to their subjects.

19. Both "At First . . ." and "Alphabet" contain a special message for young people. In your opinion, what message is each poet trying to send? Which image in each poem communicates this message to you most strongly? Why? Answer these questions in an essay. Use at least two details from each poem to support your answers.

© Pearson Education, Inc., publishing as Pearson Prentice Hall. All rights reserved.

Name _____ Date _____

Exposition: Comparison-and-Contrast Essay

Prewriting: Gathering Details

Use the following Venn diagram to gather facts, descriptions, and examples that you can use to make comparisons and contrasts. Record details in the outside sections about how each subject is different. Use the overlapping middle section to record details about how the subjects are alike.

Subject 1: _____   Subject 2: _____

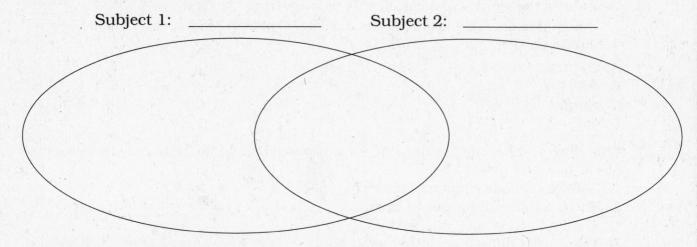

Drafting: Choosing an Organizational Pattern

Use the following graphic organizers to help you decide whether the block method or the point-by-point method is the better organizational plan for your essay.

Block Method

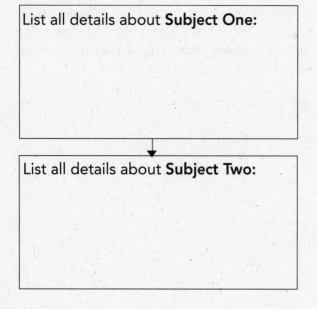

Point-by-Point Method

First Point

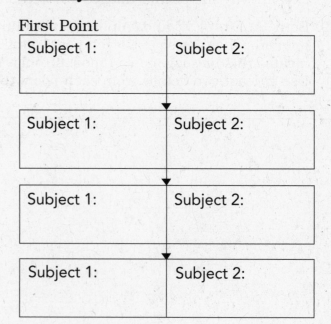

© Pearson Education, Inc., publishing as Pearson Prentice Hall. All rights reserved.

Writing Workshop—Unit 4, Part 2
Comparison-and-Contrast Essay: Integrating Grammar Skills

Revising Choppy Sentences

Complements complete the meaning of a sentence. The chart shows how combining them to create compound complements eliminates choppy sentences.

Complement	Choppy Sentences	Compound Complements
predicate adjective	Tennis is **fast-paced.** Tennis is **fun.**	Tennis is fast-paced and fun.
predicate noun	One great sport is **tennis.** Another great sport is **badminton.**	Two great sports are tennis and badminton.
direct object	Playing tennis well requires **hard work.** Playing tennis well requires **practice.**	Playing tennis well requires hard work and practice.
indirect object	Tennis helps **me** stay fit. Tennis helps **my partner** stay fit.	Tennis helps my partner and me stay fit.

Identifying Types of Compound Complements

A. DIRECTIONS: *Circle the complement in each sentence. Then, underline its type in parentheses.*

1. Football is a sport and also entertainment. (indirect objects, predicate nouns)
2. Players wear helmets and pads for protection. (direct objects, predicate nouns)
3. Injuries are usually not serious or lasting. (indirect objects, predicate adjectives)
4. Drills give the offense and the defense experience. (indirect objects, predicate nouns)

Using Compound Complements in Your Writing

B. DIRECTIONS: *On the line, rewrite the two sentences using a compound complement.*

1. Some organizations hold football camps. Some organizations hold cheerleading camps.

   _____

2. Players must be strong. Players must be fit.

   _____

3. The coach showed the quarterback a new play. The coach showed me a new play.

   _____

4. Throwing a great pass takes skill. Throwing a great pass takes practice.

   _____

© Pearson Education, Inc., publishing as Pearson Prentice Hall. All rights reserved.

Spelling Workshop—Unit 4
Affixes: Prefixes and Suffixes

Prefixes are added to the beginnings of base words, and **suffixes** are added to the ends. Prefixes do not change the spelling of the base word: *re-* + *write* = *rewrite.* Here are some changes that may happen to the base word when suffixes are added:

- If the suffix begins with a vowel, a final *e* in the base word is usually dropped: relate + ion = relation.
- If the base word ends in a consonant + *y*, the *y* usually changes to *i:* happy + ness = happiness.

Word List

betrayal	dissatisfied	furious	movement	reexamine
cleanness	education	misunderstand	plentiful	tension
joyous	stubborness	pitiful	irritation	burial

A. DIRECTIONS: *Write the word in parentheses that is spelled correctly.*

1. a (plentiful, plentyful) supply of food _____

2. to (missunderstand, misunderstand) directions _____

3. noticed the (cleanness, cleaness) of the room _____

4. a slight (movment, movement) in the trees _____

5. a high-school (educateion, education) _____

6. should (reexamine, rexamine) the evidence _____

7. a (betraïal, betrayal) of a promise _____

8. felt (dissatisfied, disatisfied) with her decision _____

B. DIRECTIONS: *Write two sentences using each group of words below.*

1. *education, misunderstand,* and *dissatisfied*

_____

_____

2. *betrayal, furious, movement,* and *tension*

_____

_____

© Pearson Education, Inc., publishing as Pearson Prentice Hall. All rights reserved.

Communications Workshop—Unit 4
Delivering a Persuasive Speech

After choosing a topic, fill out the following chart to help you organize and present your persuasive speech to the class.

Topic of persuasive speech: _____

Write a single statement to express your main idea.
How will you begin your speech to capture the audience's attention?
What key points are you going to use?
What visuals are you going to use?

© Pearson Education, Inc., publishing as Pearson Prentice Hall. All rights reserved.

For Further Reading—Unit 4

Directions: *Think about the books you have read. Then, on a separate sheet of paper, answer the discussion questions and take notes for your literature circle.*

Appreciating Poetry Prentice Hall Anthology

Discussion In "I Ask My Mother to Sing," what images does the poet use that appeal to the five senses? What is the author's message in "I Ask My Mother to Sing"?

Connections—Literature Circle Choose two poems from the same thematic category, and compare and contrast the ways in which they illustrate the theme.

Lyddie by Katherine Paterson

Discussion How would you compare and contrast the behavior and attitude of Amelia and Betsy? Which of the two young women is more like Lyddie, and in what ways?

Connections—Literature Circle What realization does Lyddie have about Luke Stevens, based on the statement that "the freight he had to fetch was human" (page 135)? What other clues are there in the book that support this realization?

Rascal by Sterling North

Discussion Would you agree with Sterling that his pets might be substitutes for a family? Explain.

Connections—Literature Circle How do the people of Brailsford Junction celebrate the end of the war? How does Sterling participate in the celebration?

Secret of the Andes by Ann Nolan Clark

Discussion Why does Chuto think that Cusi's visit to the throne is a sign? What does he think the sign tells Cusi to do?

Connections—Literature Circle What is the significance of the golden sandals? How do they help Cusi resolve his conflict in the Holy City?

© Pearson Education, Inc., publishing as Pearson Prentice Hall. All rights reserved.

Name _____ Date _____

MULTIPLE CHOICE

Reading Skills *Read the selection, and answer the questions that follow.*

> 1 All are needed by each one;
> 2 Nothing is fair or good alone.
> 3 I thought the sparrow's note from heaven,
> 4 Singing at dawn on the alder bough;
> 5 I brought him home, in his nest, at even;
> 6 He sings the song, but it cheers not now,
> 7 For I did not bring home the river and sky;—
> 8 He sang to my ear,—they sang to my eye.
>
> —from "Each and All"
> by Ralph Waldo Emerson

1. Which is the best paraphrase of lines 1 through 2 of the poem?
   A. Without charity, people would not last.
   B. There is one person who needs everything.
   C. To be fair, share what is good.
   D. All things are connected and contribute to each other's value.

2. Which of the following best states the main idea in lines 3 through 4?
   A. When the sparrow sang at dawn, I thought its song was from heaven.
   B. At dawn, I thought the note from heaven sang.
   C. I was singing at dawn in a tree when I heard the sparrow.
   D. When heaven was singing at dawn, I thought of the sparrow's note.

3. According to the speaker, why does the sparrow's song no longer cheer?
   A. The song is only inspiring when heard in its natural setting.
   B. The sparrow does not sing anymore.
   C. The speaker forgot to bring the sparrow's nest along.
   D. The speaker has grown bored of the song.

Read the selection, and answer the questions that follow.

> 1 Under a spreading chestnut-tree
> 2 The village smithy stands;
> 3 The smith, a mighty man is he,
> 4 With large and sinewy hands;
> 5 And the muscles of his brawny arms
> 6 Are strong as iron bands.
>
> —from "The Village Blacksmith"
> by Henry Wadsworth Longfellow

4. Reading this poem according to punctuation, where would you come to a complete stop?
   A. at the end of lines 2, 3, 4, and 6
   B. at the end of lines 2, 4, and 6
   C. at the end of line 6 only
   D. at the end of every line

5. Which of these should the reader do in line 5?
   A. pause briefly
   B. keep reading
   C. come to a complete stop
   D. take a lengthy pause

6. Which of the following is the best paraphrase of lines 3 through 6?
   A. The smith bends iron bands with his hands.
   B. The smith looks at the mighty man with big, strong arms.
   C. The smith is a mighty man with large hands and big, strong arms.
   D. Is the smith a mighty man with large hands and big, strong arms?

7. Which of these is an example of reading to perform a task?
   A. reading a short story
   B. reading a poem
   C. completing an application
   D. previewing informational text

8. Which part of an application might you paraphrase to make sure that you answer the questions accurately and completely?
   A. the title
   B. the return address
   C. names of contact persons
   D. the directions

9. Which task is part of previewing an application?
   A. learning whether other documents should be included
   B. filling in information on the correct lines
   C. making sure that you have completed each section
   D. signing the application, if necessary

Literary Analysis: Forms of Poetry

10. Which of these best describes a concrete poem?
    A. It is a verse form with three lines.
    B. Its shape reflects its subject.
    C. It is a funny poem of five lines.
    D. It uses rhyme and rhythm.

© Pearson Education, Inc., publishing as Pearson Prentice Hall. All rights reserved.

11. Which form describes the following poem?

> Puddle of water,
> Reflecting tree, cloud, and sky:
> The gift of new eyes.

    A. concrete poem
    B. limerick
    C. haiku
    D. nonsense poem

12. What do these lines from a poem tell you about its form?

> There once was a lad from St. Cloud,
> Whose laughter was frightfully loud.

    A. It is a haiku.
    B. It uses figurative language.
    C. It is a limerick.
    D. All of its lines rhyme.

Literary Analysis: Sound Devices *Read the selection, and answer the questions that follow.*

    1 The wind was a torrent of darkness among the gusty trees,
    2 The moon was a ghostly galleon tossed upon cloudy seas,
    3 The road was a ribbon of moonlight over the purple moor,
    4 And the highwayman came riding—
    5 Riding—riding—
    6 The highwayman came riding, up to the old inn-door.

—from "The Highwayman" by Alfred Noyes

13. Which of these is an example of alliteration in the poem?
    A. trees, seas
    B. ribbon of moonlight
    C. purple moor
    D. ghostly galleon

14. Which sound device helps create a mood of excitement and danger in the poem?
    A. onomatopoeia
    B. repetition
    C. alliteration
    D. rhyme

15. What is the most likely reason that the poet uses sound devices in this poem?
    A. to challenge the reader
    B. to express an idea
    C. to surprise the reader
    D. to express a feeling

© Pearson Education, Inc., publishing as Pearson Prentice Hall. All rights reserved.

Literary Analysis: Imagery

16. To what sense do the following lines of poetry appeal?

> She walks in beauty, like the night
> Of cloudless climes and starry skies;

> —from "She Walks in Beauty" by Lord Byron

   A. touch
   B. smell
   C. sight
   D. hearing

17. How is the sensory language in the first poem different from that in the second?

> Though the dun fox, or wild hyena, calls,
> And owls, that flit continually between,
> Shriek to the echo, and the low winds moan,
> There the true Silence is, self-conscious and alone.

> —from "Silence" by Thomas Hood

> The purple petals, fallen in the pool,
> Made the black water with their beauty gay;
> Here might the red-bird come his plumes to cool,
> And court the flower that cheapens his array.

> —from "The Rhodora"
> by Ralph Waldo Emerson

   A. The first appeals more to the sense of touch than the second.
   B. The second includes more images related to touch and taste.
   C. The second includes more images related to sight and smell.
   D. The first appeals to hearing while the second appeals to sight.

Vocabulary: Idioms

18. Which sentence contains an idiom?
   A. Amy kept her nose in a book all day.
   B. Your story is like a fairy tale.
   C. These directions are as clear as mud.
   D. The dancer's legs seemed rubbery.

19. Which of these best restates the underlined idiom in the following sentence?

   Ian got cold feet when it was his turn to speak.

   A. felt sick
   B. became stiff
   C. was prevented by fear
   D. forgot his speech

20. What is the meaning of the underlined idiom in the following sentence?

Christina was feeling <u>down in the dumps</u> after she lost the election.

   A. angry

   B. sad

   C. confused

   D. lonely

21. Which of these best restates the underlined idiom in the following sentence?

Darius finished his research report <u>ahead of time</u>.

   A. when it was due

   B. before it was due

   C. after it was due

   D. at the last moment

Grammar: Sentences

22. Which sentence contains a direct object?

   A. Sandy and Glynna are sisters.

   B. His singing voice is like butter.

   C. Today feels windier than yesterday did.

   D. Our class is raising tomatoes.

23. Which sentence contains an indirect object?

   A. Mrs. Nguyen repaired her car.

   B. Sam gave the flower to his sister.

   C. Aunt Lilly bought me a new book.

   D. The reporter asked many questions.

24. What is the direct object in the following sentence?

Tanya sent Arturo an invitation to her spring party.

   A. Tanya

   B. Arturo

   C. invitation

   D. party

25. Which sentence contains a predicate noun?

   A. This meal is very spicy.

   B. Todd's parents are doctors.

   C. The glass vase was shattered.

   D. We have missed our bus.

26. Which sentence contains a predicate adjective?

   A. E. B. White was a popular author.

   B. Computers can be frustrating.

   C. The breeze is from the south.

   D. Peonies are a type of flower.

© Pearson Education, Inc., publishing as Pearson Prentice Hall. All rights reserved.

27. What is the predicate noun in the following sentence?

    Mrs. Fox became director of the community library in our town.

    A. Mrs. Fox
    B. director
    C. library
    D. town

28. What is the best way to combine the following sentences using compound complements?

    Tony Bennett is a famous singer. He is also a talented painter.

    A. Tony Bennett is a famous singer; in addition, he is also a talented painter.
    B. Tony Bennett is a famous singer and he is a talented painter.
    C. Tony Bennett is a famous singer and a talented painter.
    D. Tony Bennett is a famous singer, and he is also a talented painter.

Spelling

29. In which sentence is the underlined word spelled correctly?
    A. Aaron <u>misspelled</u> the word *forgotten*.
    B. Mom stared at my room in <u>dissbelief</u>.
    C. Whether Mel can come is <u>unncertain</u>.
    D. I think the movie is <u>overated</u>.

30. Which sentence shows the underlined word spelled correctly?
    A. This dough is not <u>easyly</u> kneaded.
    B. Edison's <u>invenntions</u> changed lives.
    C. Oysters are a <u>seasonnal</u> food.
    D. Be sure to bring <u>comfortable</u> clothing.

31. Which sentence shows a word with the suffix *-ly* spelled correctly?
    A. The child <u>shily</u> covered her face.
    B. The weather forecast was <u>partlly</u> right.
    C. Benita gave me a <u>lovely</u> photograph.
    D. Leo <u>quickily</u> learned to play the banjo.

ESSAY

Writing

32. Suppose that you have been asked to write a limerick. Think of a humorous subject for your limerick. Write a sentence in which you tell the topic of your limerick and explain why you chose the topic. Then list two rhyming words that you might use in the limerick.

33. Suppose that you will write an essay in which you compare writing e-mails or letters with talking on the telephone. Write the headings "Similarities" and "Differences." Then list three similarities and three differences between the two forms of communication.

© Pearson Education, Inc., publishing as Pearson Prentice Hall. All rights reserved.

ANSWERS

The Poetry of Gary Soto

Vocabulary Warm-up Exercises, p. 2

A. 1. general
2. aisle
3. statue
4. pond
5. fog
6. rooster

B. Sample Answers

1. F; Something weighted down will usually sink.
2. T; A driver's hold on the wheel should never be released.
3. T; Photos should always be fingered carefully.
4. F; A snapshot makes no sounds.
5. F; Something that is tiered has more than one level.
6. F; A camera cannot be broken by the angles a photographer uses.

Reading Warm-up A, p. 3

Sample Answers

1. top-ranking officer; A *general* is a high-ranking military officer.
2. (movie theater); *Aisle* means "a passage that runs between rows of seats."
3. (thick mist); It can be hard to see in a *fog*.
4. (the famous president); A *statue* is a likeness of a person or animal made of stone.
5. he almost fell into the pond; A. J. would have felt wet—and foolish—if he had fallen into the *pond*.
6. crowed; A *rooster* is an adult male chicken.

Reading Warm-up B, p. 4

Sample Answers

1. bringing back memories of a special time; A *snapshot* is a photo.
2. (button); I *released* my hold on the ladder and jumped off.
3. (to improve the picture); *Angles* are ways of pointing a camera to get a specific shot.
4. the camera; *Fingered* means "touched repeatedly with fingers."
5. heavy equipment; I was *weighted* down with books on my walk to school today.
6. short people and small children; You would find a *tiered* seating arrangement in a theater.

Gary Soto

Listening and Viewing, p. 5

Sample answers and guidelines for evaluation:

Segment 1: The poetic language of the music of the 1960s inspired Gary Soto to begin writing poetry in high school.

Students may describe the popular music that they find inspiring and influential to them.

Segment 2: He often writes about life experiences and adds fictional details to make the poem more interesting to the reader. Students may suggest that real-life personal experiences can connect the reader to the poem, while fictional details can add emotion and excitement.

Segment 3: He uses imagery to keep the attention of the reader and make the scene more realistic. Students may answer that reading poetry can help them learn about the styles and techniques that poets use and give them ideas of what to write about.

Segment 4: Gary Soto likes to publicly present his poems and meet his readers in person. Students may answer that literature can connect people from different places and backgrounds because we are all human and like the same basic things.

Unit 4: Learning About Poetry, p. 6

A. 1. rhyme
2. onomatopoeia
3. alliteration

B. Sample Answers

1. The dog was as big as a horse.
2. Happiness is a bright sun that warms your heart.
3. I saw a sneaky snake.

The Poetry of Gary Soto

Model Selection: Poetry, p. 7

1. simile
2. Sample answer: ring, tinkle, ding
3. personification
4. **This** is the **pond,** and **these** are my **feet.**

Selection Test A, p. 8

Learning About Poetry

1. ANS: A	DIF: Easy	OBJ: Literary Analysis
2. ANS: B	DIF: Easy	OBJ: Literary Analysis
3. ANS: C	DIF: Easy	OBJ: Literary Analysis
4. ANS: A	DIF: Easy	OBJ: Literary Analysis
5. ANS: B	DIF: Easy	OBJ: Literary Analysis

Critical Reading

6. ANS: B	DIF: Easy	OBJ: Literary Analysis
7. ANS: C	DIF: Easy	OBJ: Comprehension
8. ANS: A	DIF: Easy	OBJ: Interpretation
9. ANS: B	DIF: Easy	OBJ: Comprehension
10. ANS: A	DIF: Easy	OBJ: Interpretation
11. ANS: C	DIF: Easy	OBJ: Comprehension
12. ANS: D	DIF: Easy	OBJ: Literary Analysis

© Pearson Education, Inc., publishing as Pearson Prentice Hall. All rights reserved.

13. ANS: C   DIF: Easy   OBJ: Interpretation

14. ANS: D   DIF: Easy   OBJ: Interpretation

Essay

15. Students will probably say that the saleslady is kind and understanding. She knows that the boy doesn't have enough money to pay for the chocolate, but she protects his pride and accepts his orange as payment. She knows that he wants to buy a treat for the girl and that he is probably embarrassed that he can't pay for it.

    Difficulty: *Easy*

    Objective: *Essay*

16. Answers will vary but should present clear explanations for the choice supported by details from the selected poem.

    Difficulty: *Easy*

    Objective: *Essay*

Selection Test B, p. 11

Learning About Poetry

1. ANS: C	DIF: Average	OBJ: Literary Analysis
2. ANS: B	DIF: Challenging	OBJ: Literary Analysis
3. ANS: D	DIF: Average	OBJ: Literary Analysis
4. ANS: A	DIF: Average	OBJ: Literary Analysis
5. ANS: C	DIF: Average	OBJ: Literary Analysis
6. ANS: D	DIF: Challenging	OBJ: Literary Analysis

Critical Reading

7. ANS: C	DIF: Average	OBJ: Literary Analysis
8. ANS: B	DIF: Average	OBJ: Literary Analysis
9. ANS: D	DIF: Challenging	OBJ: Literary Analysis
10. ANS: C	DIF: Challenging	OBJ: Comprehension
11. ANS: B	DIF: Average	OBJ: Comprehension
12. ANS: B	DIF: Average	OBJ: Literary Analysis
13. ANS: C	DIF: Average	OBJ: Interpretation
14. ANS: A	DIF: Challenging	OBJ: Interpretation
15. ANS: C	DIF: Average	OBJ: Comprehension
16. ANS: B	DIF: Average	OBJ: Comprehension
17. ANS: C	DIF: Challenging	OBJ: Literary Analysis
18. ANS: C	DIF: Average	OBJ: Comprehension

Essay

19. Students should base their summaries on the events described in the poem, told from the point of view of the saleslady. Most students will say that she felt sympathetic toward the boy.

    Difficulty: *Average*

    Objective: *Essay*

20. Students will probably say that the photos are important because they are records of happy times the family shared. The people in the photos are all smiling and laughing, and many of the photos are taken on family trips to parks and zoos.

    Difficulty: *Average*

    Objective: *Essay*

21. Answers will vary but should present a clear explanation supported by details from the selected poem.

    Difficulty: *Challenging*

    Objective: *Essay*

Unit 4, Part 1 Answers

Diagnostic Test 7, p. 15

MULTIPLE CHOICE

1. ANS: D
2. ANS: B
3. ANS: C
4. ANS: A
5. ANS: D
6. ANS: B
7. ANS: C
8. ANS: B
9. ANS: D
10. ANS: B
11. ANS: B
12. ANS: A
13. ANS: D
14. ANS: C
15. ANS: A

Poetry Collection: Ogden Nash, Jack Prelutsky, and Rosemary and Stephen Vincent Benét

Vocabulary Warm-up Exercises, p. 19

A.
1. cross
2. discouraged
3. confident
4. bulged
5. praised
6. daring

B. Sample Answers
1. No. A car could not fit into a bag the size of a small suitcase.
2. No. You might be loyal to a friend, but not to an enemy.

© Pearson Education, Inc., publishing as Pearson Prentice Hall. All rights reserved.

3. No. Fortresses are strong and built to withstand attacks.

4. No. A glider does not have an engine.

5. I would call half a sandwich a minuscule dinner.

6. You might want to murmur when talking in a library or in a movie theater.

Reading Warm-up A, p. 20

Sample Answers

1. brave; I think it is an act of *daring* to try something you have not done before.

2. (a forehead); *Bulged* means "to stick out or swell out."

3. (sure); Scientists were *confident* that the monster didn't exist.

4. (for putting an end to a story that wasn't true); *Praised* means "given compliments."

5. mad; I would feel *cross* if someone was telling lies about me.

6. They still think that the monster is hiding in the lake; *Discouraged* means "feeling as if you have no more enthusiasm for something."

Reading Warm-up B, p. 21

Sample Answers

1. an engine; A *glider* is a small plane that does not have an engine.

2. (since there was no engine); I could only *murmur* the words since I had a sore throat.

3. (building better planes); *Devoted* means "loyal to a person, thing, or idea."

4. The cockpits were tiny; A *satchel* is a small bag.

5. heavily protected; In the *fortress*, people were safe from the storm because the building was so strong.

6. other planes; *Tiny*, *small*, and *little* are similar to *minuscule* in meaning.

Poetry Collection: Jack Prelutsky, Rosemary and Stephen Vincent Benét, Ogden Nash

Reading: Ask Questions to Use Context Clues, p. 22

Sample Answers

Question / Answer / Meaning

2. Which words describe it? / "tail," "gristle," "bone" / stick; club

3. What kind of word is it? / It is an adjective. It describes how you feel about something that is unpleasant and does not stop. / bothersome; annoying

4. What words can I use in place of this expression? / not easy / not easy

5. What kind of word is it? / It is an adjective. It describes a witch's face. / mean; grouchy

Literary Analysis: Rhythm and Rhyme, p. 23

Note: Teachers may want to point out that in item 3, *horrid / forehead* is not an exact rhyme. Nash often uses near rhymes for comic effect. They might also point out that some lines in "Adventures of Isabel" have an irregular rhythm, but there are still four stressed syllables in each line.

Words that students are to circle appear in parentheses. Students need not scan lines with complete accuracy.

Sample Answers

1. AN-ky-lo-SAUR-us was BEST left (a-LONE) / Its TAIL was a CUD-gel of GRIS-tle and (BONE)

2. They GLI-ded HERE, they GLI-ded (THERE) / They SOME-times SKINNED their (NO-ses). / For LEARN-ing HOW to RULE the (AIR) / Was NOT a BED of (RO-ses)

3. The GI-ant was HAIR-y, the GI-ant was (HOR-rid), / He HAD one EYE in the MID-dle of his (FORE-head). / Good MOR-ning IS-a-bel, the GI-ant (SAID), / I'll GRIND your BONES to MAKE my (BREAD).

Vocabulary Builder, p. 24

A. 1. ravenous
  2. inedible
  3. rancor

B. Sample Answers

1. Someone might be *ravenous* after a long, difficult hike.

2. Someone might feel *rancor* if he or she had seen someone being cruel to an animal.

3. Food that is moldy would be considered *inedible*.

C. 1. B; 2. D; 3. C

Enrichment: Keys to Success, p. 27

A. Sample Answers

1. The person meeting this challenge could use resourcefulness to think of ways to earn money for the ticket. A resourceful student might think of jobs such as mowing lawns, shoveling snow, washing cars, or babysitting. Determination could help the student save his or her allowance and earnings instead of spending them on snacks, movies, or video games.

2. Resourcefulness would help a student think of ways to rehearse in front of increasingly larger, more critical audiences. A student might tape his or her performance as well as the comments. Self-confidence and determination would help the student overcome nervousness.

B. Students should write about using resourcefulness to meet a challenge. They should recognize the importance of self-confidence in exerting leadership. They should recognize that determination will help them achieve the goal despite feelings of discouragement and obstacles.

© Pearson Education, Inc., publishing as Pearson Prentice Hall. All rights reserved.

Selection Test A, p. 28

Critical Reading

1. ANS: B DIF: Easy OBJ: Literary Analysis
2. ANS: C DIF: Easy OBJ: Interpretation
3. ANS: C DIF: Easy OBJ: Comprehension
4. ANS: A DIF: Easy OBJ: Reading
5. ANS: B DIF: Easy OBJ: Interpretation
6. ANS: D DIF: Easy OBJ: Literary Analysis
7. ANS: B DIF: Easy OBJ: Reading
8. ANS: C DIF: Easy OBJ: Comprehension
9. ANS: D DIF: Easy OBJ: Comprehension
10. ANS: D DIF: Easy OBJ: Interpretation
11. ANS: A DIF: Easy OBJ: Interpretation

Vocabulary and Grammar

12. ANS: B DIF: Easy OBJ: Vocabulary
13. ANS: C DIF: Easy OBJ: Vocabulary
14. ANS: A DIF: Easy OBJ: Vocabulary
15. ANS: B DIF: Easy OBJ: Grammar

Essay

16. Students should name one of the poems and cite three reasons for finding it funny. For "Ankylosaurus," they might mention the *clankity* sound that the dinosaur makes, the comparison of the dinosaur to a tank, and the reference to its "minuscule mind." If they choose "Wilbur Wright and Orville Wright," they might note that the brothers are made to seem silly (for example, by complaining that the birds "are very trying"), that their attempts at flying are made to seem like child's play ("They sometimes skinned their noses"), and that the rhymes are unusual (for example, *grant / shan't* and *little shop / soda-pop*). If they choose "Adventures of Isabel," they might note the contradictions in Isabel's character (she is neat and efficient, but as ruthless and mean as her enemies), the surprise at the end of each stanza, and the repetition of humorous lines ("Isabel, Isabel, didn't worry," and so on).
Difficulty: *Easy*
Objective: *Essay*

17. Students may mention that Isabel and the Wrights are fearless and confident. They are different in that Isabel depends only on herself, while the Wrights encourage each other and are loyal to each other. Students might also mention that Isabel is fierce and probably mean. The Wrights, on the other hand, are not aggressive. Finally, students might point out that the Wrights are inventors, involved in a creative pursuit, while Isabel spends her time getting into and out of trouble.
Difficulty: *Easy*
Objective: *Essay*

Selection Test B, p. 31

Critical Reading

1. ANS: C DIF: Average OBJ: Literary Analysis
2. ANS: C DIF: Average OBJ: Comprehension
3. ANS: D DIF: Challenging OBJ: Reading
4. ANS: C DIF: Average OBJ: Literary Analysis
5. ANS: B DIF: Challenging OBJ: Literary Analysis
6. ANS: D DIF: Challenging OBJ: Reading
7. ANS: B DIF: Average OBJ: Interpretation
8. ANS: C DIF: Average OBJ: Literary Analysis
9. ANS: C DIF: Average OBJ: Reading
10. ANS: B DIF: Average OBJ: Interpretation
11. ANS: D DIF: Average OBJ: Interpretation
12. ANS: D DIF: Average OBJ: Comprehension
13. ANS: A DIF: Average OBJ: Interpretation

Vocabulary and Grammar

14. ANS: B DIF: Average OBJ: Vocabulary
15. ANS: C DIF: Average OBJ: Vocabulary
16. ANS: A DIF: Average OBJ: Grammar
17. ANS: B DIF: Average OBJ: Grammar

Essay

18. Students should name one of the poems and cite reasons for finding it funny. For "Ankylosaurus," for example, they might mention the poet's description of the noise the dinosaur makes when it walks, the repeated comparison of the Ankylosaurus to a tank, and perhaps the rhyming of "sturdy as steel" with "an inedible meal." They may say that they like the rhythm of the poem because it seems to move like a dinosaur, with heavy steps; they may point out that almost all of the end rhymes are simple, one-syllable words, like *clank* and *tank;* and they may note that the rhymes seem to reinforce the humorous image of a big, small-brained dinosaur.
Difficulty: *Average*
Objective: *Essay*

19. Students should point to at least one detail in each poem that hints at the setting. For example, in "Ankylosaurus" they might point to the Ankylosaurus itself; in "Wilbur Wright and Orville Wright" they might point to the dusty little bicycle-repair shop, and in "Adventures of Isabel" they might point to the pitch-dark night. Students may choose the poem about the Wright brothers as the one they think most successfully evokes a place, with its "dusty little shop" and drinks of "soda-pop." In any case, they should defend their choice with references to the poem.
Difficulty: *Average*
Objective: *Essay*

© Pearson Education, Inc., publishing as Pearson Prentice Hall. All rights reserved.

Poetry Collection: Edgar Allan Poe, Maya Angelou, and Lewis Carroll

Vocabulary Warm-up Exercises, p. 35

A. 1. clasp
2. maids
3. spoil
4. might
5. weep
6. overhead

B. Sample Answers
1. Some people carry a rabbit's foot as a lucky <u>charm</u> to make sure nothing bad happens.
2. It was Bob's first time away from home, so <u>parting</u> from his family was hard.
3. Sheila is a <u>pitiless</u> person; she doesn't care if anyone else is unhappy.
4. My sister went to her room <u>sulkily</u> because she wasn't very happy with her gift.
5. Why did you bring me such small <u>quantities</u>? I told you I needed a lot.
6. At a wedding, the bride and the groom <u>avow</u> their love for each other.

Reading Warm-up A, p. 36

Sample Answers
1. <u>ruin</u>; Rain might *spoil* an outdoor party.
2. (orange and black streamers); *Overhead* means "above."
3. (mops, brooms, and buckets); *Maids* do housecleaning work.
4. (her pet); *Clasp* means "grip" or "hold."
5. <u>keep the tears from flowing</u>; I would *weep* if someone stole my bicycle.
6. <u>screamed</u>; *Might* means "strength, force, or ability."

Reading Warm-up B, p. 37

Sample Answers
1. <u>good luck</u>; Some people carry a lucky stone as a *charm*.
2. (amount); I have large *quantities* of pennies that I keep in jars.
3. (run away); *Sulkily* means "in a way that shows unhappiness."
4. <u>staying</u>; *Parting* means "the act of leaving."
5. <u>cruel</u>; In movies, villains are often *pitiless* characters.
6. <u>you will not be afraid to try new activities or ask others for help</u>; *Avow* means "to promise or say something publicly."

Poetry Collection: Maya Angelou, Edgar Allan Poe, Lewis Carroll

Reading: Ask Questions to Use Context Clues, p. 38

Sample Answers
Question / Answer / Meaning
2. What word can I use in place of it? / admit; tell / admit
3. What kind of word is it? / It names something below a person's hand at the beach. / the ocean
4. Which other words in the sentence explain it? / "a tighter clasp" / grip; hold
5. What kind of word is it? / It names something that is not smooth and that the sun shines on over the sea. / waves

Literary Analysis: Rhythm and Rhyme, p. 39

Note: Teachers may wish to point out that *scream / dreams* in item 1 is an approximate rhyme. Another example of such a rhyme is *smile / wild* in lines 19–20.

Words that students are to circle appear in parentheses. Students need not scan lines with complete accuracy.

Sample Answers
1. Don't SHOW me FROGS and SNAKES / And LIS-ten FOR my (SCREAM), / If I'M a-FRAID at ALL / It's ON-ly IN my (DREAMS).
2. All THAT we SEE or (SEEM) / Is BUT a DREAM with-IN a (DREAM).
3. "The TIME has COME," the WAL-rus SAID, / "To TALK of MA-ny (THINGS): / Of SHOES—and SHIPS—and SEAL-ing WAX—/ Of CAB-ba-GES—and (KINGS)—"

Vocabulary Builder, p. 40

A. 1. beseech
2. quantities
3. dismal
4. deem

B. 1. C; 2. A; 3. D; 4. B

Enrichment: Science and Nonsense, p. 43

A. 1. Oysters have no developed eyes or head.
2. They could not wear coats, and they do not have faces.

B. 1. The Walrus asks whether seven maids with seven mops could clear away the sand in half a year.
2. Students might mention any number of "impossible tasks" in the Harry Potter books and in modern fairy

© Pearson Education, Inc., publishing as Pearson Prentice Hall. All rights reserved.

tales such as *Shrek.* They may also mention the search for the Holy Grail in the King Arthur legend or the legendary feats of Paul Bunyan.

3. Students may describe a task like finding a food crop that would solve the problem of world hunger or finding a way for large numbers of people to travel to, explore, and settle on other planets.

Poetry Collections: Jack Prelutsky, Rosemary and Stephen Vincent Benét, Ogden Nash; Maya Angelou, Edgar Allan Poe, Lewis Carroll

Build Language Skills: Vocabulary, p. 44

Prefixes

A. Sample Answers

1. Before a plane taxis down a runway, the captain does a preflight check of the instrument panel.
2. Preteens enjoy going to movies, shopping at the mall, and attending high-school sports events.
3. In prehistoric times, dinosaurs roamed Earth.

B. Sample Answers

1. F; People watch a movie preview to decide whether they want to see the movie. If the preview told how the movie ended, people would not want to see the movie.
2. F; A restatement retells something in your own words, so a restatement of a poem would probably be about as long as the original poem.
3. F; When you use the context to figure out the meaning of a word, you look at the other words in the sentence and at the sentences around the one in which the word appears.
4. F; When you define an unfamiliar word, you look it up in a dictionary. A dictionary contains definitions.
5. F; It would not be easy to make a nonsense poem clear or understandable because nonsense does not make sense; it has no meaning.

Build Language Skills: Grammar, p. 45

Sentences: Simple and Compound Subjects

A. 1. <u>Animals</u> and <u>people</u> are good subjects for poems.
2. After dinner, will <u>you</u> or <u>Robert</u> put away the leftovers?
3. <u>Everyone</u> should come up with a plan.
4. Every spring, hungry <u>deer</u> and <u>raccoons</u> invade our garden in search of food.
5. On a counter in the kitchen, <u>flour</u>, <u>sugar</u>, and <u>butter</u> are waiting to be made into cookies.
6. <u>Lewis Carroll</u> may well be my favorite poet.

B. Students should write a cohesive, grammatically correct paragraph in which they describe two subjects they would write poems about. They should write at least one sentence that has a simple subject and two sentences that have a compound subject. They should underline the subject of every sentence.

Poetry Collection: Maya Angelou, Edgar Allan Poe, Lewis Carroll

Selection Test A, p. 46

Critical Reading

1. ANS: B	DIF: Easy	OBJ: Literary Analysis
2. ANS: B	DIF: Easy	OBJ: Comprehension
3. ANS: D	DIF: Easy	OBJ: Interpretation
4. ANS: C	DIF: Easy	OBJ: Literary Analysis
5. ANS: A	DIF: Easy	OBJ: Comprehension
6. ANS: A	DIF: Easy	OBJ: Interpretation
7. ANS: D	DIF: Easy	OBJ: Reading
8. ANS: B	DIF: Easy	OBJ: Interpretation
9. ANS: C	DIF: Easy	OBJ: Comprehension
10. ANS: D	DIF: Easy	OBJ: Reading
11. ANS: B	DIF: Easy	OBJ: Interpretation

Vocabulary and Grammar

12. ANS: B	DIF: Easy	OBJ: Vocabulary
13. ANS: D	DIF: Easy	OBJ: Vocabulary
14. ANS: D	DIF: Easy	OBJ: Grammar
15. ANS: A	DIF: Easy	OBJ: Grammar

Essay

16. Students should state the title of the poem they like most and identify two elements they enjoyed. For example, in "Life Doesn't Frighten Me," they may like the repetition of the title line, the natural sound of the poem, the confidence of the speaker, or the end rhymes. In "A Dream Within a Dream," they may like the emotion, the "romantic" mood, the image of grains of sand slipping through the speaker's fingers, and the image of the "surf-tormented shore." In "The Walrus and the Carpenter," they may like the humor, the nonsensical lines (such as the Walrus's talk of "cabbages and kings"), the nonsensical images (oysters dressed up for a picnic), the regular rhythm, and the dialogue.

Difficulty: *Easy*
Objective: *Essay*

17. Students should describe the trick that the Walrus and the Carpenter play on the oysters. They should explain their reasons for finding the poem completely humorous or somewhat serious. Students who see a serious side to the poem may say that it makes the point that one should not trust strangers.

Difficulty: *Easy*
Objective: *Essay*

Selection Test B, p. 49

Critical Reading

1. ANS: C	DIF: Challenging	OBJ: Reading
2. ANS: C	DIF: Average	OBJ: Literary Analysis

© Pearson Education, Inc., publishing as Pearson Prentice Hall. All rights reserved.

3. ANS: A	DIF: Average	OBJ: Comprehension	
4. ANS: B	DIF: Average	OBJ: Comprehension	
5. ANS: D	DIF: Average	OBJ: Literary Analysis	
6. ANS: C	DIF: Average	OBJ: Literary Analysis	
7. ANS: D	DIF: Average	OBJ: Reading	
8. ANS: B	DIF: Average	OBJ: Interpretation	
9. ANS: C	DIF: Average	OBJ: Comprehension	
10. ANS: B	DIF: Average	OBJ: Reading	
11. ANS: D	DIF: Average	OBJ: Interpretation	
12. ANS: A	DIF: Average	OBJ: Literary Analysis	
13. ANS: A	DIF: Average	OBJ: Interpretation	

Vocabulary and Grammar

14. ANS: A	DIF: Average	OBJ: Vocabulary	
15. ANS: D	DIF: Challenging	OBJ: Vocabulary	
16. ANS: B	DIF: Average	OBJ: Grammar	
17. ANS: B	DIF: Average	OBJ: Grammar	

Essay

18. Students who choose "Life Doesn't Frighten Me" should recognize that the speaker seems to be a young girl: She is not afraid that boys might pull her hair. She seems to scorn "kissy little girls," so she may be a tomboy. She seems to have read a lot: She knows about dragons and panthers. She has a vivid imagination: She imagines walking on the ocean floor and having a magic charm. Students who choose "A Dream Within a Dream" should recognize that the speaker seems to be a man who is parting from a woman he has loved. He is sad. He calls upon God and weeps as he compares life to grains of sand slipping through his fingers. Students who choose "The Walrus and the Carpenter" might be inclined to say that the speaker is a man because the author is a man. They should recognize that the speaker has a sense of humor and a penchant for nonsense (oysters wear clean, neat shoes but have no feet) and does not seem to blame the Walrus and the Carpenter for tricking the Oysters.

Difficulty: *Average*

Objective: *Essay*

19. Students should recognize that the speaker in "Life Doesn't Frighten Me" looks forward to the future because she believes she has nothing to fear. They may cite any number of lines from the poem to support this point. Students should recognize that the speaker in "A Dream Within a Dream" is weak and fearful, looking only on the dark side of life. The speaker says that nothing he or she loves in life lasts. The speaker seems sad, comparing the precious things in life to grains of sand slipping though his or her fingers. To this speaker, life is dangerous and threatening (for example, even the shore is "surf-tormented").

Difficulty: *Average*

Objective: *Essay*

Poetry Collection: Eve Merriam, Emily Dickinson, and Langston Hughes

Vocabulary Warm-up Exercises, p. 53

A. 1. pools
2. chorus
3. streaming
4. delicate
5. silken
6. sketch

B. Sample Answers
1. F; Jumping in a puddle in a <u>gutter</u> at the side of the road will probably make you dirtier.
2. F; After being covered with <u>liquid</u>, a person will feel wet.
3. T; The rarer something is, the more <u>precious</u> it is.
4. T; A bee and a wasp both have a <u>sting</u>.
5. T; Someone who works hard deserves a reward.
6. F; If a person has <u>fame</u>, it means that many people know who they are.

Reading Warm-up A, p. 54

Sample Answers
1. <u>small bodies of water</u>; <u>ponds</u>; *Pools* are small bodies of water.
2. (fine and fragile); I think flower petals are *delicate*.
3. (soft, shiny); The *silken* fabric was soft and pleasing to touch.
4. <u>makes the branches bend and sway</u>; When something is *streaming*, it is moving in a smooth and continuous way.
5. <u>the noise of the wind in the branches</u>; I only know the words to the *chorus* of the song.
6. (an artist's rough drawing); An artist can use a *sketch* to help plan a painting.

Reading Warm-up B, p. 55

Sample Answers
1. <u>soak Rita's hair and clothing</u>; The juice from any fruit is *liquid*.
2. (few); (valuable); The diamond was rare and *precious*.
3. <u>well known</u>; *Fame* is not something I would like to have because I like going places and not being noticed.
4. (by the side of the road); On my way to school, I tripped off the sidewalk and fell into the *gutter*.
5. <u>small and sharp</u>; Having a *sting* is what lets a bee cause a sharp pain.
6. <u>After being soaked in the rain, she felt that she deserved to spend her afternoon pampering herself</u>; A person who tries extra hard and a person who has been in an emergency are *worthy* of special treatment.

© Pearson Education, Inc., publishing as Pearson Prentice Hall. All rights reserved.

Poetry Collection: Eve Merriam,
Emily Dickinson, Langston Hughes

Reading: Reread and Read Ahead to Find and Use Context Clues, p. 56

Sample Answers

Context clues / Meaning in context / Second meaning

2. "green and gold" / beautiful / just
3. "rain," "liquid drops" / shiny, like the color of silver / coins made of silver
4. "pools on the sidewalk" / quiet, having no action / yet; continuing

Literary Analysis: Figurative Language, p. 57

A. Phrases students should underline are followed by the letters identifying the figurative language:

fell like flower petals, S; was a surprising gift, M; like a machine, S; was a kindly messenger, M; telling me to forget my worries, P

B. Sample Answers

Type / What It Does / What It Shows

2. simile / It compares the tree to a city child. / It shows where the ginkgo grows.
3. metaphor / It compares the sky to metal. / It shows the color of an overcast sky.
4. personification / It compares the rain to a parent. / It shows that rain is kind.

Vocabulary Builder, p. 58

A. 1. chorus
2. thrives
3. thrives
4. chorus

B. Sample Answers

1. The singer would sing in a group because a chorus is a group of people who sing together.
2. A dog thrives in human company because it is bred to be a pet. A bear is a wild animal; it does not thrive among humans.

C. 1. B; 2. A

Enrichment: Science, p. 61

A. 1. The willow is a broadleaf tree. It grows in North America; it changes color ("Wherever it grows, there is green and gold and fair"); its branches hang down ("The willow dips to the water").
2. Sample answer: The ginkgo "grows up in the street. . . . / Somehow it survives and even thrives."

B. Students might consult the Web site of the National Arbor Day Foundation for photographs of willows and ginkgoes. They will most likely illustrate the weeping willow, nearly as broad as it is tall. Its branches sweep the ground; its leaves are long and green gray in color.

The ginkgo is neither as tall nor as broad. Its branches grow outward and upward. It has a round or pyramid shape and fan-shaped leaves that are green in summer, yellow in fall.

Selection Test A, p. 62

Critical Reading

1. ANS: D	DIF: Easy	OBJ: Comprehension
2. ANS: A	DIF: Easy	OBJ: Literary Analysis
3. ANS: C	DIF: Easy	OBJ: Reading
4. ANS: B	DIF: Easy	OBJ: Interpretation
5. ANS: B	DIF: Easy	OBJ: Interpretation
6. ANS: C	DIF: Easy	OBJ: Comprehension
7. ANS: C	DIF: Easy	OBJ: Literary Analysis
8. ANS: A	DIF: Easy	OBJ: Literary Analysis
9. ANS: B	DIF: Easy	OBJ: Reading
10. ANS: D	DIF: Easy	OBJ: Interpretation
11. ANS: C	DIF: Easy	OBJ: Interpretation

Vocabulary and Grammar

12. ANS: B	DIF: Easy	OBJ: Vocabulary
13. ANS: D	DIF: Easy	OBJ: Vocabulary
14. ANS: A	DIF: Easy	OBJ: Vocabulary
15. ANS: C	DIF: Easy	OBJ: Grammar

Essay

16. Students should recognize that the speaker in "Simile" believes that the willow is the more beautiful tree but prefers the ginkgo because it is tougher; they should understand that the speaker in "Fame Is a Bee" sees fame as good in some ways, bad in others; or they should recognize that the speaker in "April Rain Song" has a deep appreciation of rain. Students should express their opinion on these topics and express agreement or disagreement with the speaker, citing two reasons for their response.

Difficulty: *Easy*

Objective: *Essay*

17. Students should briefly explain why the poem they chose is their favorite. For example, they might like the comparison between the two trees in "Simile," the ideas about fame expressed in "Fame Is a Bee," or the way in which rain is described in "April Rain Song." They should then identify one figure of speech in the poem and explain what they liked about it.

Difficulty: *Easy*

Objective: *Essay*

Selection Test B, p. 65

Critical Reading

1. ANS: D	DIF: Average	OBJ: Comprehension
2. ANS: C	DIF: Average	OBJ: Reading

© Pearson Education, Inc., publishing as Pearson Prentice Hall. All rights reserved.

3. **ANS:** A	**DIF:** Average	**OBJ:** Literary Analysis
4. **ANS:** A	**DIF:** Average	**OBJ:** Interpretation
5. **ANS:** B	**DIF:** Average	**OBJ:** Interpretation
6. **ANS:** A	**DIF:** Average	**OBJ:** Reading
7. **ANS:** B	**DIF:** Challenging	**OBJ:** Literary Analysis
8. **ANS:** D	**DIF:** Average	**OBJ:** Interpretation
9. **ANS:** D	**DIF:** Average	**OBJ:** Literary Analysis
10. **ANS:** B	**DIF:** Average	**OBJ:** Reading
11. **ANS:** A	**DIF:** Average	**OBJ:** Literary Analysis
12. **ANS:** A	**DIF:** Average	**OBJ:** Interpretation
13. **ANS:** D	**DIF:** Average	**OBJ:** Interpretation

Vocabulary and Grammar

14. **ANS:** B	**DIF:** Average	**OBJ:** Vocabulary
15. **ANS:** A	**DIF:** Average	**OBJ:** Vocabulary
16. **ANS:** C	**DIF:** Average	**OBJ:** Vocabulary
17. **ANS:** D	**DIF:** Challenging	**OBJ:** Grammar

Essay

18. Students should identify a simile in "Simile," a metaphor in "Fame Is a Bee," or personification in "April Rain Song" and explain what is being compared and what is shown. They should offer a clear and thoughtful reason for liking the figure of speech they chose to write about.

Difficulty: *Average*

Objective: *Essay*

19. Students writing about "Simile" should recognize that the basic comparison involves nature. They might cite the willow and ginkgo or any other reference to nature (the calf, the bull, the water, the sky). Students writing about "Fame Is a Bee" should recognize that the metaphor involves an insect. They might cite the bee, its song (a buzz), its sting, and its wing. Students writing about "April Rain Song" should refer to the rain and perhaps its drops, the sounds as it falls (it beats, it sings), and the pools it forms.

Difficulty: *Average*

Objective: *Essay*

Poetry Collection: Sandra Cisneros, Nikki Giovanni, and Theodore Roethke

Vocabulary Warm-up Exercises, p. 69

A. 1. rushing
2. snores
3. accusers
4. dough
5. doorknob
6. without

B. Sample Answers
1. If I lost a pencil <u>underneath</u> my desk, I would have to reach down below my desk to find it.
2. Wet leaves would not make a <u>crackling</u> sound if I stepped on them because <u>crackling</u> is a sharp, crisp sound.
3. If a stone is <u>streaked</u>, that means it is probably striped with different colors.
4. When I <u>receive</u> a gift, I get to keep it because it has been given to me.
5. <u>Splinters</u> are small because they are thin, sharp pieces of wood.

Reading Warm-up A, p. 70

Sample Answers
1. <u>pale yellow paste</u>; Cookies and pizza crust are made by baking *dough.*
2. <u>His heavy breathing could be heard throughout the house;</u> (He makes a noise just like a truck)
3. (to open the living room door); I turned the *doorknob* to open the door to my bedroom.
4. <u>They knew they had been caught, and they could not leave quickly enough.</u>; My father always seems to be *rushing* to work because he is late.
5. <u>they were responsible for getting the two in trouble</u>; *Accusers* are people who charge someone with doing something wrong.
6. (a hug from me); I would be unhappy *without* my bicycle.

Reading Warm-up B, p. 71

Sample Answers
1. (Reflecting light); *Flashing* light appears and disappears suddenly, and that is why people notice it.
2. (warmth is trapped), (plants can be grown in a stable and warm atmosphere); The ground is *underneath* my feet.
3. <u>proper care</u>; When you *receive* something, it is given to you.
4. (sharp), (quick), (sound); A burning fire makes a *crackling* sound.
5. <u>If it gets too warm, the wood will dry out and can break</u>; *Splinters* create a sharp pain when they get stuck in my skin.
6. (rich, even color); It was hard to see through the *streaked* glass.

Poetry Collection: Sandra Cisneros,
Nikki Giovanni, Theodore Roethke

Reading: Reread and Read Ahead to Find and Use Context Clues, p. 72

Sample Answers

Context clues / Meaning in context / Second Meaning

2. "you are my" / a precious jewel / a four-sided figure
3. "my britches" / the part you rest on when sitting / a chair
4. "of elms" / row / occupation

Literary Analysis: Figurative Language, p. 73

A. Phrases students should underline are followed by the letters identifying the figurative language:

like hammers, S; as heavy as rocks, S; fountain that welcomes, P; was an oasis in the desert, M

B. Sample Answers

Type / What It Does / What It Shows

2. personification / It compares the ocean to a person. / It claims that the behavior of the ocean depends on the clouds.
3. simile / It compares elm trees to horses. / It shows the up-and-down movement of the branches in a strong wind.

Vocabulary Builder, p. 74

A. 1. plunging
2. billowing
3. billowing
4. plunging

B. Sample Answers

1. If I saw smoke billowing from the windows of a house, I would think there might be a fire. I would call the fire department. I would bang on the door to see if anyone was inside and wait outside for help.
2. Yes, I would buy a computer if prices were plunging, because that would mean prices were going down.

C. 1. B; 2. D

Enrichment: Elder Care, p. 77

A. Sample Answers

1. Advantages might include having someone readily available who has time to spend with the children in the house, playing games, talking, and maybe even helping with homework; having someone available who can share memories and wisdom; and having the opportunity to help and care for an older person.
2. Disadvantages might include having less privacy, having less leisure time, needing to remain quiet so as not to disturb the relative, and feeling sad should the relative become seriously ill or disabled.

B. Students should list three skills or personal qualities that they think someone who works with the elderly should have, such as patience and understanding, a sense of humor, an ability to cook, and a driver's license.

C. Sample Questions

1. Why do you want to work with an elderly person?
2. What experience have you had working with the elderly?
3. What would you do to entertain an elderly person who is housebound?

Poetry Collections: Eve Merriam, Emily
Dickinson, Langston Hughes; Sandra Cisneros,
Nikki Giovanni, Theodore Roethke

Build Language Skills: Vocabulary, p. 78

A. 1. retraced
2. reunite
3. replaced
4. refuel

B. Sample Answers

1. We wanted to see the movie because we had seen a *preview* of it.
2. The teachers *restate* what they have already said.
3. I can *explain* anything I understand.
4. To figure out the meaning of a word from its *context*, look at the words and sentences in the surrounding text.
5. If you want to *define* a word, you should give its meaning.

Build Language Skills: Grammar, p. 79

Sentence Functions

A. 1. exclamatory
2. imperative
3. declarative
4. imperative
5. interrogative

B. Students should write cohesive, grammatically correct paragraphs in which they use, correctly identify, and correctly capitalize and punctuate the four kinds of sentences. Sample answer: What fun that was! (E) I liked the poems we read. (D) Did you like any of them? (Int) I am going to the library to get some poetry books. (D) Please come with me. (Imp)

© Pearson Education, Inc., publishing as Pearson Prentice Hall. All rights reserved.

Poetry Collection: Sandra Cisneros,
Nikki Giovanni, Theodore Roethke

Selection Test A, p. 80

Critical Reading

1. ANS: C   DIF: Easy   OBJ: Comprehension
2. ANS: D   DIF: Easy   OBJ: Comprehension
3. ANS: A   DIF: Easy   OBJ: Literary Analysis
4. ANS: B   DIF: Easy   OBJ: Interpretation
5. ANS: D   DIF: Easy   OBJ: Literary Analysis
6. ANS: D   DIF: Easy   OBJ: Interpretation
7. ANS: A   DIF: Easy   OBJ: Reading
8. ANS: A   DIF: Easy   OBJ: Interpretation
9. ANS: D   DIF: Easy   OBJ: Interpretation
10. ANS: A   DIF: Easy   OBJ: Interpretation
11. ANS: C   DIF: Easy   OBJ: Interpretation

Vocabulary and Grammar

12. ANS: D   DIF: Easy   OBJ: Vocabulary
13. ANS: A   DIF: Easy   OBJ: Vocabulary
14. ANS: C   DIF: Easy   OBJ: Vocabulary
15. ANS: D   DIF: Easy   OBJ: Grammar

Essay

16. Students should explain the thoughts or feelings of the speaker in one of the poems in the collection. Those who choose "Abuelito Who," for example, might write that the speaker feels sad because she can no longer play with her grandfather. She loved him because he was kind and said nice things to her. Now he is sick, perhaps close to death. The speaker repeats what her grandfather said: "who loves him?" The speaker loves him and misses him.
    Difficulty: *Easy*
    Objective: *Essay*

17. Students should name one of the poems and cite at least one line from it that explains why they liked it. Students who choose "Abuelito Who" may say that the poem reminds them of a favorite relative or a relative who died. Students who choose "The World Is Not a Pleasant Place to Be" may say that they, too, find that having a companion makes life bearable. Students who choose "Child on Top of a Greenhouse" may say that they like the way the speaker describes an exciting experience from the viewpoint of a child.
    Difficulty: *Easy*
    Objective: *Essay*

Selection Test B, p. 83

Critical Reading

1. ANS: A   DIF: Average   OBJ: Interpretation
2. ANS: C   DIF: Average   OBJ: Comprehension
3. ANS: B   DIF: Average   OBJ: Comprehension
4. ANS: B   DIF: Average   OBJ: Literary Analysis
5. ANS: A   DIF: Average   OBJ: Comprehension
6. ANS: D   DIF: Average   OBJ: Literary Analysis
7. ANS: D   DIF: Average   OBJ: Comprehension
8. ANS: A   DIF: Average   OBJ: Interpretation
9. ANS: D   DIF: Challenging   OBJ: Literary Analysis
10. ANS: C   DIF: Average   OBJ: Reading
11. ANS: A   DIF: Average   OBJ: Interpretation
12. ANS: A   DIF: Challenging   OBJ: Literary Analysis
13. ANS: C   DIF: Average   OBJ: Interpretation
14. ANS: B   DIF: Average   OBJ: Interpretation

Vocabulary and Grammar

15. ANS: D   DIF: Average   OBJ: Vocabulary
16. ANS: D   DIF: Average   OBJ: Vocabulary
17. ANS: B   DIF: Average   OBJ: Vocabulary
18. ANS: A   DIF: Average   OBJ: Grammar

Essay

19. Students should identify the two speakers they have chosen to compare and contrast and should cite two details about each one. A student who chooses "Abuelito Who" and "Child on Top of a Greenhouse," for example, should recognize that both speakers are children. They might note that the speakers differ in that one is concerned about the illness of her grandfather whereas the other is exulting in having climbed to the roof of a greenhouse.
    Difficulty: *Average*
    Objective: *Essay*

20. Students should note that the speaker in "Abuelito Who" would probably say that the presence of Abuelito makes the world pleasant. The speaker in "The World Is Not a Pleasant Place to Be" similarly believes that the world is not pleasant if one does not have a companion. The speaker in "Child on Top of a Greenhouse" might say that adventure is what makes the world pleasant.
    Difficulty: *Average*
    Objective: *Essay*

© Pearson Education, Inc., publishing as Pearson Prentice Hall. All rights reserved.

Poetry by Robert Frost and E.E. Cummings

Vocabulary Warm-up Exercises, p. 87

A. 1. mood
2. rued
3. keen
4. shook
5. saved
6. themselves

B. Sample Answers

1. Jose <u>filled</u> his backpack by putting all his books in it.
2. As Evan walked up the staircase, he was moving <u>higher</u> in the building.
3. Melanie liked <u>sailing</u>, so she sailed in her boat across the lake.
4. Because Luke <u>always</u> enjoyed reading, he made sure to take out books from the library.
5. The pilot inflated the hot-air <u>balloon</u> with a light gas so that it could fly.

Reading Warm-up A, p. 88

Sample Answers

1. <u>A mood is the state of mind you are in at a specific moment in time.</u>; Most people enjoy being in a good *mood*.
2. (intensely); My dog has a *keen* sense of smell.
3. (regret); I *rued* the day I forgot to hand in my homework.
4. (their hands); I *shook* out the rug to get rid of the dust.
5. <u>unwanted bad moods</u>; To have *saved* someone means that you have prevented something bad from happening to that person.
6. <u>People who are in good moods</u>; I think most people feel good about *themselves*.

Reading Warm-up B, p. 89

Sample Answers

1. <u>Hot-air balloons are large sacks made out of cloth that are pumped full of a gas that's lighter than air.</u>; I would not like to ride in a hot-air *balloon* because I am afraid of heights.
2. (catches the wind and moves through the air much like a ship moves across the sea); *Sailing* means moving through the power of the wind.
3. (hot gas); The swimming pool was *filled* with water during the summer.
4. <u>If the gas is not lighter than the air at all times, the balloon will sink.</u>; I *always* need to wear my watch so I know what time it is.
5. <u>moves upward into the sky</u>; I climbed *higher* toward the top of the jungle gym.
6. (many beautiful locations); Last year, I *visited* the Grand Canyon.

Poetry by Robert Frost and E.E. Cummings

Literary Analysis: Imagery, p. 90

Sample Answers

A. 1. movement, sound, sight
2. movement, touch, sight
3. movement, sight
4. sight
5. movement, sight
6. sight, touch

B. 1. lightheartedness; surprise; joy
2. fancifulness; escape; happiness; playfulness; peacefulness

Vocabulary Builder, p. 91

A. 1. steeples
2. rued

B. Sample Answers

1. When she saw the poor grade on her paper, Kayla *rued* her preparation for the test.
2. It is easy to see the churches' *steeples* from a distance.

C. 1. D; 2. B

Selection Test A, p. 93

Critical Reading

1. ANS: C	DIF: Easy	OBJ: Comprehension
2. ANS: B	DIF: Easy	OBJ: Literary Analysis
3. ANS: D	DIF: Easy	OBJ: Comprehension
4. ANS: A	DIF: Easy	OBJ: Comprehension
5. ANS: A	DIF: Easy	OBJ: Literary Analysis
6. ANS: C	DIF: Easy	OBJ: Literary Analysis
7. ANS: B	DIF: Easy	OBJ: Interpretation
8. ANS: D	DIF: Easy	OBJ: Comprehension
9. ANS: C	DIF: Easy	OBJ: Literary Analysis
10. ANS: C	DIF: Easy	OBJ: Interpretation
11. ANS: A	DIF: Easy	OBJ: Interpretation
12. ANS: B	DIF: Easy	OBJ: Interpretation
13. ANS: D	DIF: Easy	OBJ: Interpretation
14. ANS: B	DIF: Easy	OBJ: Literary Analysis

Vocabulary

15. ANS: D	DIF: Easy	OBJ: Vocabulary

Essay

16. Students should respond that in "Dust of Snow," the speaker is having a bad day until a crow in a tree shakes some snow down on him, an act that makes him feel cheerful. Students should respond that in "who

knows if the moon's," the speaker sees the moon in a new way—as a balloon that might carry him to a city in the sky. Students should describe a nature experience of their own and explain which speaker's experience is most similar as well as how it is similar.

Difficulty: *Easy*
Objective: *Essay*

17. Students should respond that in "Dust of Snow," the main word picture is of a crow in a snowy hemlock tree; or, alternatively, of a dusting of snow falling on the speaker. These word pictures appeal primarily to the senses of sight and touch. Students should respond that in "who knows if the moon's," the main word picture is of the bright moon-balloon in the sky. This word picture appeals primarily to the senses of sight and movement.

Difficulty: *Easy*
Objective: *Essay*

Selection Test B, p. 96

Critical Reading

1. ANS: A	DIF: Average	OBJ: Comprehension
2. ANS: D	DIF: Average	OBJ: Literary Analysis
3. ANS: B	DIF: Challenging	OBJ: Literary Analysis
4. ANS: A	DIF: Average	OBJ: Literary Analysis
5. ANS: C	DIF: Challenging	OBJ: Interpretation
6. ANS: D	DIF: Challenging	OBJ: Comprehension
7. ANS: D	DIF: Average	OBJ: Literary Analysis
8. ANS: C	DIF: Average	OBJ: Interpretation
9. ANS: A	DIF: Average	OBJ: Interpretation
10. ANS: C	DIF: Challenging	OBJ: Literary Analysis
11. ANS: C	DIF: Average	OBJ: Literary Analysis
12. ANS: B	DIF: Average	OBJ: Interpretation
13. ANS: A	DIF: Average	OBJ: Interpretation
14. ANS: C	DIF: Challenging	OBJ: Literary Analysis
15. ANS: A	DIF: Average	OBJ: Comprehension

Vocabulary

16. ANS: D	DIF: Average	OBJ: Vocabulary
17. ANS: C	DIF: Average	OBJ: Vocabulary

Essay

18. Students may point out that in "Dust of Snow," Frost helps readers see nature as playful; he does so by describing in clear and simple terms how a crow shook some snow onto him and in this way dispelled the gloomy mood he had been in. Students may point out that in "who knows if the moon's," Cummings helps readers see the moon as a fantastical escape; he does so by imagining it as a balloon that transports people to a

magical city. Accept other reasonable responses that are supported by details from the poems.

Difficulty: *Average*
Objective: *Essay*

19. Students who choose to be a painter may be drawn most strongly to the image of the crow in the snowy tree in Frost's poem or to the moon in the night sky in Cummings's poem. Students who choose to be a musician may be drawn most strongly to the image of the shaking branches and the quiet sound of snow falling in Frost's poem. Students who choose to be a dancer may be drawn most strongly to the fluttering crow or the falling snow in Frost's poem, or to the upwardly floating balloon in Cummings's poem. Students' reasons for being drawn to these images will vary. Accept all reasonable responses that are supported by details from the poems.

Difficulty: *Average*
Objective: *Essay*

20. Students should note that in "Dust of Snow," the speaker is a person who is walking through the woods, and he meets nature when a crow rustles in a tree and causes snow to fall on him. This meeting changes the speaker by lifting his spirits. Students should note that in "who knows if the moon's," the speaker is a person who seems to want to escape the everyday world. He meets nature when he sees the moon and imagines it to be a balloon that will carry him away. He seems soothed and uplifted by the meeting. Students should identify the speaker with which they identify more strongly, and explain why.

Difficulty: *Challenging*
Objective: *Essay*

Writing Workshop—Unit 4, Part 1

Writing for Assessment: Integrating Grammar Skills, p. 100

A. 1. imperative; . 2. question; ? 3. declarative; .
   4. exclamatory; !

B. 1. Has methane gas recently been detected on Mars?
   2. Mars is the planet most like Earth.
   3. It is 47 million miles from Earth to Mars!
   4. Be prepared for lower gravity if you go to Mars.

Unit 4, Part 1 Answers

Benchmark Test 7, p. 101

MULTIPLE CHOICE

1. ANS: C
2. ANS: D
3. ANS: D
4. ANS: B
5. ANS: A

6. ANS: B

7. ANS: B

8. ANS: C

9. ANS: D

10. ANS: A

11. ANS: B

12. ANS: B

13. ANS: C

14. ANS: A

15. ANS: C

16. ANS: B

17. ANS: C

18. ANS: D

19. ANS: B

20. ANS: A

21. ANS: B

22. ANS: C

23. ANS: B

24. ANS: D

25. ANS: A

26. ANS: A

27. ANS: B

28. ANS: C

29. ANS: A

30. ANS: D

31. ANS: C

ESSAY

32. Students' sentences should be clear and complete. They should contain the name of a literary work and express a general opinion of it.

33. Students' diagrams should show aspects of one or more types of weather and should contain at least one example of simile, metaphor, or personification.

34. Students should clearly state three supporting details related to the main idea.

Unit 4, Part 2 Answers

Diagnostic Test 8, p. 108

MULTIPLE CHOICE

1. ANS: A

2. ANS: B

3. ANS: C

4. ANS: D

5. ANS: A

6. ANS: C

7. ANS: B

8. ANS: D

9. ANS: B

10. ANS: A

11. ANS: B

12. ANS: A

13. ANS: C

14. ANS: D

15. ANS: C

Poetry Collection: Bashō, Anonymous, and Lillian Morrison

Vocabulary Warm-up Exercises, p. 112

A. 1. sailor

2. sea

3. splash

4. flee

5. skimming

6. caught

B. Sample Answers

1. Buy a mirror without a <u>flaw</u> in it to make sure you can see yourself clearly.

2. The <u>asphalt</u> pavement was as hard as cement.

3. Stop yelling and screaming; I need <u>silence</u>.

4. We built a strong, solid building out of bricks to make sure it would not <u>sway</u> in the breeze.

5. My bike began to <u>swerve</u> on the wet part of the road.

6. I hate noise when I am studying, so I study far away from that <u>whirring</u> clock.

Reading Warm-up A, p. 113

Sample Answers

1. <u>ocean</u>; When the *sea* is rough, you shouldn't go swimming.

2. (nonstop whining); *Flee* means "to escape or run away."

3. (gliding); You might see skaters *skimming* across the ice.

4. (a girl, about his age, throwing a fishing line into the bay); *Splash* is the sound something makes when it hits the water.

5. <u>a fishing boat</u>; A *sailor* might work on a Coast Guard boat.

6. <u>rock</u>; *Caught* means "trapped or stuck."

Reading Warm-up B, p. 114

Sample Answers

1. <u>parking lots</u>; A playground could be *asphalt*.

2. (the top); You might find near *silence* in a library.

3. (wheels on the track); A wind-up toy might make a *whirring* sound.

© Pearson Education, Inc., publishing as Pearson Prentice Hall. All rights reserved.

4. to the side; *Swerve* means "turn sharply and suddenly."
5. as they rocket down a wooden track; *Sway* means "to move back and forth."
6. on the track; *Flaw* means "break or crack."

Poetry Collection: Bashō, Anonymous, Lillian Morrison

Reading: Reread to Paraphrase, p. 115
Sample Answers

1. swerve: turn aside suddenly / I turn quickly, move in a curve and back and forth
2. silent: quiet / an old totally quiet pond . . .
3. flue: chimney / a flea and a fly were caught in a chimney
4. flaw: crack / a crack in the chimney

Literary Analysis: Forms of Poetry, p. 116
Sample Answers

1. Line 1—See: a pond; hear: stillness
   Line 2—See: a frog jumping in; hear: nothing
   Line 3—See: the splash of water; hear: splash, then stillness
2. A flea and a fly in a flue   *a*
   Were caught, so what could they do?   *a*
       Said the fly, "Let us flee."   *b*
       "Let us fly," said the flea.   *b*
   So they flew through a flaw in the flue.   *a*
3. Sample answers: a clock, a pencil, a mouse

Vocabulary Builder, p. 117

A. A crow on a flue belching smoke
Said, "Something's amiss, that's no joke.
What a flaw in the day,
I'll go skimming away
If I don't flee this flue, I will choke."

B. Sample Answers

1. flaw—Syn.: mistake
2. flee—Def.: run away; Syn.: escape; Sentence: They managed to flee the burning house.
3. skimming—Def.: moving on the surface; Syn.: gliding; Sentence: The skaters, skimming across the ice, raced to the finish line.

Enrichment: Poetic Art, p. 120

The artwork should show contrast in style and spirit. The haiku sketch should illustrate something about the haiku. The comic strip should show the action and dialogue of the limerick, using dialogue balloons or captions.

Selection Test A, p. 121
Critical Reading

1. ANS: B	DIF: Easy	OBJ: Literary Analysis
2. ANS: A	DIF: Easy	OBJ: Comprehension
3. ANS: D	DIF: Easy	OBJ: Interpretation
4. ANS: B	DIF: Easy	OBJ: Reading
5. ANS: C	DIF: Easy	OBJ: Literary Analysis
6. ANS: A	DIF: Easy	OBJ: Literary Analysis
7. ANS: C	DIF: Easy	OBJ: Literary Analysis
8. ANS: D	DIF: Easy	OBJ: Interpretation
9. ANS: A	DIF: Easy	OBJ: Comprehension
10. ANS: B	DIF: Easy	OBJ: Reading

Vocabulary and Grammar

11. ANS: C	DIF: Easy	OBJ: Vocabulary
12. ANS: B	DIF: Easy	OBJ: Vocabulary
13. ANS: D	DIF: Easy	OBJ: Grammar
14. ANS: C	DIF: Easy	OBJ: Grammar

Essay

15. Student essays should identify and describe the setting of each poem: outdoor, peaceful, nature setting of the haiku; busy, fast-moving, city setting of "The Sidewalk Racer." Essays should explain which setting students prefer, and why. For example, the haiku is about places outdoors that are so quiet one can hear the splash of a frog jumping into water; or "The Sidewalk Racer" is about busy city streets where something new and exciting is always happening.
    Difficulty: *Easy*
    Objective: *Essay*
16. Student essays should identify one poem the student wishes he or she had written and include reasons why he or she would be proud to have written that poem. For example, students may write that they like the way the haiku presents a snapshot of a scene in a few words; that the limerick would be complicated to write because it has so many rules to be "obeyed," but it remains humorous; or that the shape of a concrete poem shows its subject.
    Difficulty: *Easy*
    Objective: *Essay*

Selection Test B, p. 124
Critical Reading

1. ANS: C	DIF: Average	OBJ: Reading
2. ANS: B	DIF: Average	OBJ: Comprehension
3. ANS: D	DIF: Average	OBJ: Literary Analysis

4. ANS: B	DIF: Average	OBJ: Interpretation
5. ANS: C	DIF: Challenging	OBJ: Literary Analysis
6. ANS: D	DIF: Challenging	OBJ: Literary Analysis
7. ANS: B	DIF: Average	OBJ: Reading
8. ANS: C	DIF: Average	OBJ: Comprehension
9. ANS: A	DIF: Average	OBJ: Literary Analysis
10. ANS: A	DIF: Average	OBJ: Comprehension
11. ANS: D	DIF: Average	OBJ: Interpretation
12. ANS: A	DIF: Average	OBJ: Literary Analysis
13. ANS: C	DIF: Challenging	OBJ: Reading
14. ANS: B	DIF: Average	OBJ: Interpretation

Vocabulary and Grammar

15. ANS: C	DIF: Average	OBJ: Vocabulary
16. ANS: B	DIF: Average	OBJ: Vocabulary
17. ANS: A	DIF: Average	OBJ: Grammar

Essay

18. Student essays should compare and contrast any two poetry forms. If they compare haiku and limerick forms, essays should relate the number of lines and syllables in each line, point out that limericks have a special rhyming scheme while the lines of haiku do not rhyme, and note that the two forms are similar in that they have strict requirements concerning the number of lines and syllables in each line of a haiku and the number of lines and the rhyming pattern in a limerick. The forms are different. Haiku is serious, while the limerick is humorous or nonsense verse. Language in haiku is simple and spare, while language in limericks has rhymes and double meanings that add to the poem's humor. Essays should include words or lines from both poems to support student opinions.

Difficulty: *Average*
Objective: *Essay*

19. Student essays should summarize one poem and include an explanation of why it was memorable.

Difficulty: *Average*
Objective: *Essay*

Poetry Collection: Soseki, Anonymous, and Dorthi Charles

Vocabulary Warm-up Exercises, p. 128

A. 1. dish
2. stripes
3. forest
4. spring
5. paw
6. whisker

B. Sample Answers

1. mishaps; If you were careful, you wouldn't have so many mishaps.
2. deadly; Three people died in the deadly crash.
3. guy; That jacket is for a guy, not a girl.
4. roar; When the elephants roar like that, it's pretty loud.
5. fury; Being treated so badly sent him into a fury.
6. chilly; This chilly wind makes me want to go back inside where it's warm.

Reading Warm-up A, p. 129

Sample Answers

1. long, stiff hair that sticks out from a cat's face; A walrus has more than one *whisker* on its face.
2. (scratches at a tree); A *paw* is one kind of animal foot.
3. (in their fur); *Stripes* are long, narrow bands of color.
4. (woods); A *forest* has lots of trees.
5. dinner; A *dish* is a bowl or container used to serve food.
6. water; I drink bottled water that comes from a *spring*.

Reading Warm-up B, p. 130

Sample Answers

1. ice storms, freezing rain, blizzards; *Wintry* means "cold and snowy."
2. (The winds); When in a *rage*, a person feels very angry.
3. (in the early part of the week); *Accidents* are unplanned events in which people are hurt or things are damaged.
4. deadly; Plane crashes are often *fatal*.
5. (pain); To *howl* means "to make a roaring, screaming, or whining noise."
6. man; *Guy, boy*, and *male* are similar to *fellow* in meaning.

Poetry Collection: Soseki, Anonymous, Dorthi Charles

Reading: Reread to Paraphrase, p. 131

Sample Answers

1. blow: move with some force / there are no leaves left that they can blow down from the trees
2. fellow: boy or man / a young man named Hall
3. spring: a season, or a flow of water from the ground; fall: autumn / who fell into the water during the autumn

Literary Analysis: Forms of Poetry, p. 132

Sample Answers

1. Line 1—See: snow on the ground; hear: nothing; feel: cold

Line 2—See: many trees; hear: howling wind; feel: cold wind blowing

© Pearson Education, Inc., publishing as Pearson Prentice Hall. All rights reserved.

Line 3—See: bare branches bending in the wind; hear: nothing; feel: cold

2. There <u>was</u> a young <u>fellow</u> named <u>Hall</u>,   *a*
Who <u>fell</u> in the <u>spring</u> in the <u>fall</u>;   *a*
  'Twould have <u>been</u> a sad <u>thing</u>   *b*
  If he <u>died</u> in the <u>spring</u>,   *b*
But he <u>didn't</u>—he <u>died</u> in the <u>fall</u>.   *a*

3. Sample answers: a clock, a pencil, a mouse

Vocabulary Builder, p. 133

A. A silly young <u>fellow</u> named Phil
Used to <u>howl</u> at the moon on the hill
So a wolf in a <u>rage</u>
Shut Phil up in a cage
'Til Phil made a vow to be still.

B. Sample Answers

1. rage—syn.: anger
2. howl—Def.: make a loud wailing cry; Syn.: wail; Sentence: We could hear the howl of the storm and the pounding of the rain.
3. fellow—Def.: boy or man, a comrade; Syn.: person; Sentence: Who was that fellow with you at the game?

Enrichment: Poetic Art, p. 136

The artwork should show contrast in style and spirit. The haiku sketch should illustrate something about the haiku. The comic strip should show the action and dialogue of the limerick, using dialogue balloons or captions.

Poetry Collections: Bashō, Anonymous, Lillian Morrison; Soseki, Anonymous, Dorthi Charles

Build Language Skills: Vocabulary, p. 137

Idioms

A. Sample Answers

1. relax
2. get some sleep
3. watch
4. stay up late

B. 1. F; Conveying the main idea of a narrative poem takes more than one word because it requires a complete sentence.
2. T; A haiku suggests a lot in three short lines; it might take several sentences to explain its meaning.
3. F; When you paraphrase a poem, you use prose, not poetry.
4. T; Rereading a difficult passage is the first step to understanding it.
5. T; If you didn't represent the author's ideas correctly, you would not be fair to the author.

Build Language Skills: Grammar, p. 138

Subject Complements: Direct and Indirect Objects

A. 1. <u>haiku</u>; <u>teacher</u>; Direct object answers *What?* Indirect object answers *To whom?*
2. <u>phone</u>; <u>Sally</u>; Direct object answers *What?* Indirect object answers *To whom?*
3. <u>note</u>; <u>teacher</u>; Direct object answers *What?* Indirect object answers *To whom?*

B. Sample Answers

1. I bought <u>myself</u> some <u>jeans</u> and a <u>sweater</u>.
2. Mom found my <u>brother</u> a <u>T-shirt</u> she thought he'd like.
3. We owed the <u>store</u> <u>fifty dollars</u>!
4. Mom gave the <u>clerk</u> her <u>credit card</u>.

Poetry Collection: Soseki, Anonymous, Dorthi Charles

Selection Test A, p. 139

Critical Reading

1. ANS: B	DIF: Easy	OBJ: Comprehension
2. ANS: A	DIF: Easy	OBJ: Comprehension
3. ANS: A	DIF: Easy	OBJ: Reading
4. ANS: C	DIF: Easy	OBJ: Reading
5. ANS: B	DIF: Easy	OBJ: Literary Analysis
6. ANS: D	DIF: Easy	OBJ: Literary Analysis
7. ANS: D	DIF: Easy	OBJ: Interpretation
8. ANS: A	DIF: Easy	OBJ: Literary Analysis
9. ANS: D	DIF: Easy	OBJ: Interpretation
10. ANS: B	DIF: Easy	OBJ: Reading
11. ANS: C	DIF: Easy	OBJ: Interpretation

Vocabulary and Grammar

12. ANS: C	DIF: Easy	OBJ: Vocabulary
13. ANS: C	DIF: Easy	OBJ: Reading

Essay

14. Student essays should discuss one of the poetic forms and make three statements about it that tell how that form is different from the other forms. For example, a haiku has three lines, is usually about nature, and has a certain number of syllables in each line; the limerick form is usually a silly poem that has five lines, with certain lines that rhyme, and may include words with double meanings; the concrete poem has a shape that suggests its subject.
Difficulty: *Easy*
Objective: *Essay*

15. Student essays should identify one poetic form and include reasons for that choice. For example, haiku might be chosen because they are short poems about nature and forces of nature such as wind and rain; limericks because they are funny poems that are like riddles or jokes that have clever ways of putting words together; or concrete poems because they combine words with the shape of a subject.

Difficulty: *Easy*

Objective: *Essay*

Selection Test B, p. 142

Critical Reading

1. ANS: B	DIF: Average	OBJ: Comprehension
2. ANS: C	DIF: Challenging	OBJ: Reading
3. ANS: D	DIF: Average	OBJ: Literary Analysis
4. ANS: A	DIF: Average	OBJ: Interpretation
5. ANS: D	DIF: Challenging	OBJ: Literary Analysis
6. ANS: D	DIF: Challenging	OBJ: Literary Analysis
7. ANS: B	DIF: Average	OBJ: Reading
8. ANS: A	DIF: Average	OBJ: Comprehension
9. ANS: C	DIF: Average	OBJ: Interpretation
10. ANS: A	DIF: Average	OBJ: Literary Analysis
11. ANS: A	DIF: Average	OBJ: Interpretation
12. ANS: B	DIF: Average	OBJ: Interpretation
13. ANS: A	DIF: Average	OBJ: Interpretation
14. ANS: B	DIF: Challenging	OBJ: Reading Skill

Vocabulary and Grammar

15. ANS: C	DIF: Average	OBJ: Vocabulary
16. ANS: D	DIF: Average	OBJ: Vocabulary
17. ANS: C	DIF: Average	OBJ: Grammar

Essay

18. Student essays should identify one poem as most difficult and another poem as the easiest to paraphrase. Choices most likely will be "Concrete Cat" as most difficult because this poem is visual rather than verbal. Essays will most likely discuss the haiku as easiest to paraphrase because it is a short poem that is easier to understand and reword than the limerick, with its double meanings.

Difficulty: *Average*

Objective: *Essay*

19. Student essays should identify one poetic form as the one they would find the most interesting to write. Reasons cited in the essay might include that the haiku form is a three-lined poem that conveys a vivid image and has a certain number of syllables in each line; limericks are funny poems with rhyming lines and double

meanings; and concrete poetry expresses the visual as well as the written word.

Difficulty: *Average*

Objective: *Essay*

Poetry Collection: Shel Silverstein, Octavio Paz, and Rachel Field

Vocabulary Warm-up Exercises, p. 146

A.
1. meowing
2. dispersed
3. allergies
4. clawed *or* scratched
5. scratched *or* clawed
6. disappear

B. Sample Answers
1. The artist <u>sculpted</u> the three-dimensional sculpture out of clay.
2. The teacher did not take the right medicine and quickly <u>developed</u> a nasty cough.
3. The actor on the stage appeared <u>motionless</u> when he stood very still.
4. I reached <u>beneath</u> my desk to place my book under it.
5. The baker <u>hollowed</u> out a loaf of bread by pulling out the middle of it.

Reading Warm-up A, p. 147

Sample Answers
1. <u>give them to people who will love and take care of the animals as pets</u>; *Dispersed* means "sent away in many directions."
2. (sounds); I don't like the sound of *meowing* because I don't like cats.
3. (dig through the dirt with their claws); The raccoon *clawed* a hole in the garbage bag.
4. (never be found again) If something does *disappear*, it vanishes without a trace.
5. <u>because they are afraid of you</u>; Once, I was *scratched* by the branches of a tree.
6. <u>bodily reactions can cause someone to sneeze</u>; My father has bad *allergies* in the spring when pollen is in the air.

Reading Warm-up B, p. 148

Sample Answers
1. <u>stands still</u>; If something is *motionless*, it means that it is not moving.
2. (shape the stone); I *sculpted* a clay figure in art class.
3. <u>the land and stone of the riverbed</u>; My chair and the floor are *beneath* me right now.

© Pearson Education, Inc., publishing as Pearson Prentice Hall. All rights reserved.

4. a deep riverbed; My brother *developed* a dislike of apples as he grew older.

5. (Over millions of years, the Colorado River dug a deep pit through the center of its riverbed); If something has been *hollowed*, an empty space has been made in the middle of it.

6. continuous, rhythmic; The *beating* drums made me want to get up and dance.

Poetry Collection: Shel Silverstein, Octavio Paz, and Rachel Field

Reading: Read Aloud According to Punctuation to Paraphrase, p. 149

A. 2. SP
3. DS
4. DS
5. FS; DS
6. LP

B. Sample Answer

A good reader should not stop between lines 3 and 4 because there is no punctuation mark. Not stopping gives the line more meaning.

Literary Analysis: Sound Devices, p. 150

A. 2. midnight meowing mews; R, A, O
3. Water and wind and stone; R, A
4. murmurs; O
5. With blare of brass, with beating drums; R, A, O
6. roar; O (Note that "clashing cymbals" is not alliterative. The consonant *c* has the sound of /k/ in *clashing* and the sound of /s/ in *cymbals*.)

B. Sample Answers

1. Repetition: chased each other, pounced on each other, raced with each other; as tame as tame
2. Alliteration: funny balls of fluff; Felicity, the feral cat
3. Onomatopoeia: purring; squeaky

Vocabulary Builder, p. 151

A. Sample Answers

1. F; The children would be unlikely to return after thunder had *dispersed* them because thunder signals the approach of a storm.
2. F; If a student *murmurs* answers, the teacher will not hear them well.
3. T; If the child is moving in a *leisurely* way before school, he will likely miss the bus.

B. Sample Answers

1. Students *dispersed* throughout the school to hand out election information.
2. A father *murmurs* to his son, "I think I'll order dessert. How about you?"

3. On weekends we have a *leisurely* breakfast and talk about the week's events.

C. 1. C; 2. A; 3. D

Enrichment: The Circus, p. 154

A. Sample Answers

Sight: performers, animals, red and gold wagons, horses, clowns, dancers

Sound: music, sounds of animals, laughter

Smell: animals, popcorn, peanuts

Touch: sticky cotton candy

Taste: cotton candy, popcorn, peanuts

B. Ancient Rome: chariot races, horses, trained animals

Middle Ages: trained animals, jugglers, tightrope walkers, music, clowns, dancers

Modern Times: horses, trained animals, jugglers, tightrope walkers, parades, music, clowns, dancers

Selection Test A, p. 155

Critical Reading

1. ANS: B	DIF: Easy	OBJ: Comprehension
2. ANS: A	DIF: Easy	OBJ: Interpretation
3. ANS: D	DIF: Easy	OBJ: Literary Analysis
4. ANS: D	DIF: Easy	OBJ: Comprehension
5. ANS: C	DIF: Easy	OBJ: Literary Analysis
6. ANS: B	DIF: Easy	OBJ: Reading
7. ANS: D	DIF: Easy	OBJ: Interpretation
8. ANS: B	DIF: Easy	OBJ: Reading
9. ANS: A	DIF: Easy	OBJ: Interpretation
10. ANS: B	DIF: Easy	OBJ: Literary Analysis

Vocabulary and Grammar

11. ANS: D	DIF: Easy	OBJ: Vocabulary
12. ANS: A	DIF: Easy	OBJ: Vocabulary
13. ANS: C	DIF: Easy	OBJ: Vocabulary
14. ANS: D	DIF: Easy	OBJ: Grammar

Essay

15. Student essays should discuss one sound device using examples from any of the poems. The alliteration in "No Thank You" is one element that makes the poem humorous. For example, "midnight, meowing mews" and "scratchin', snarlin', spitters" are unusual, funny ways to describe kittens. The alliteration in "Parade" helps create the sound of a parade passing by, with "blare of brass and beating drums." The repetition in "No Thank You" emphasizes the speaker's humorous comments about kittens and other pets: "No more smell of kitty litter,/No more mousies in my bed." The ono-

matopoeia in "Parade," such as "blare," "beating," and "roar," makes the reader "hear" the sounds of the passing parade.

Difficulty: *Easy*

Objective: *Essay*

16. Student essays should mention one "sight" from the poem—for example, shiny cages, horses and riders, fun-shaped floats, clowns, and animals. Sounds might be blare of horns, beating drums, clashing cymbals, roar of wild beasts. Essays should also include students' own ideas of smells and tastes found at a parade.

Difficulty: *Easy*

Objective: *Essay*

Selection Test B, p. 158

Critical Reading

1. ANS: B	DIF: Average	OBJ: Comprehension
2. ANS: A	DIF: Average	OBJ: Interpretation
3. ANS: B	DIF: Average	OBJ: Literary Analysis
4. ANS: B	DIF: Average	OBJ: Reading
5. ANS: C	DIF: Average	OBJ: Interpretation
6. ANS: D	DIF: Average	OBJ: Literary Analysis
7. ANS: B	DIF: Challenging	OBJ: Interpretation
8. ANS: C	DIF: Average	OBJ: Reading
9. ANS: A	DIF: Challenging	OBJ: Reading
10. ANS: C	DIF: Average	OBJ: Comprehension
11. ANS: B	DIF: Average	OBJ: Interpretation
12. ANS: A	DIF: Challenging	OBJ: Literary Analysis
13. ANS: C	DIF: Challenging	OBJ: Literary Analysis

Vocabulary and Grammar

14. ANS: B	DIF: Average	OBJ: Vocabulary
15. ANS: A	DIF: Average	OBJ: Vocabulary
16. ANS: C	DIF: Average	OBJ: Vocabulary
17. ANS: A	DIF: Average	OBJ: Grammar

Essay

18. Student essays might discuss the use of repetition in "No Thank You," as almost every line repeats with humorous effect a phrase in another line; the repetition of grammatical constructions, such as "room for mice and gerbils" and "beds for boars and bats"; the use of alliteration for humorous effect, as in "midnight meowing mews" and "scratchin', snarlin', spitters"; the onomatopoeia in "Parade," with the use of *blare, beating, clashing,* and *roar.*

Difficulty: *Average*

Objective: *Essay*

19. Student essays should explain that a poem should be read according to its punctuation because a poem makes more sense that way. Readers should not pause,

for instance, at the end of a line that has no punctuation because it would be confusing to stop in the middle of a sentence. The sentence is completed on a following line. In "Parade," for instance, essays might cite "Within town limits. Spick and span" as an example of a line that loses its meaning if the reader fails to stop at the period. "Spick and span" begins another sentence. In "Wind and water and stone," most of the lines end with a comma, a slight pause, with a long pause at the end of each stanza. In the fourth stanza, it is important for the reader not to stop after "among their empty names" because the next two lines complete the sentence.

Difficulty: *Average*

Objective: *Essay*

Poetry Collection: William Shakespeare, Diana Chang, Gwendolyn Brooks

Vocabulary Warm-up Exercises, p. 162

A. 1. lullaby
2. approach
3. melody
4. loudness
5. charm
6. rather

B. Sample Answers

1. F; If an animal is <u>spotted</u>, it has areas of different colors on its body.
2. T; <u>Thorny</u> plants can scratch you.
3. T; <u>Weaving</u> can create cloth or webs or baskets.
4. F; If you <u>actually</u> believe something, you really think it's true.
5. T; If someone <u>hushes</u> you, they want you to be quiet.
6. F; <u>Whiteness</u> is the state of being white or blank.

Reading Warm-up A, p. 163

Sample Answers

1. <u>moved closer</u>; I always feel happy when I *approach* a candy store.
2. (the tune helped her fall asleep); My favorite *lullaby* as a child was a folk song that my father would sing to me.
3. (toned down; softer and softer); *Loudness* is a high level of noise.
4. <u>tune</u>; The *melody* of the song on the radio stuck in my head.
5. <u>you</u>; I would *rather* go to the beach than go to the mountains.
6. (She was pleased); When I want to *charm* somebody, I speak to him or her about subjects I know that person enjoys.

© Pearson Education, Inc., publishing as Pearson Prentice Hall. All rights reserved.

Reading Warm-up B, p. 164

Sample Answers

1. <u>color</u>; The *whiteness* of the snow dazzled my eyes.
2. (scratch them and tear their clothes); I would not like to touch something that is *thorny* because I might hurt myself while touching it.
3. <u>silly</u>; A synonym for *actually* is *really*.
4. (into silence); *Hushes* means "asks to be quiet."
5. (make webs); *Weaving* looms can be big machines.
6. <u>marked with spots</u>; My face is *spotted* with freckles.

Poetry Collection: William Shakespeare, Diana Chang, Gwendolyn Brooks

Reading: Read Aloud According to Punctuation, p. 165

A. 2. DS
3. FS
4. SP
5. FS

B. Sample Answer

A good reader will not stop between lines 2 and 3 because there is no punctuation mark there. Not stopping gives the sentence more meaning.

Literary Analysis: Sound Devices, p. 166

A. 2. <u>Lulla, lulla, lullaby, lulla, lulla, lullaby</u>; R, A
3. <u>"Yes", "Yes"</u>; R
4. <u>Not neither-nor not</u>; R, A
5. <u>SUSHES</u>; O
6. <u>whitely whirs</u>; A, O

B. Sample Answers

1. repetition: no star-gazing, no night hike, and no campfire; drip, drip, drip
2. alliteration: scrambled into our sleeping bags; big, brown bear
3. onomatopoeia: drip, drip, drip; banged; crashed

Vocabulary Builder, p. 167

A. Sample Answers

1. I would feel tired because I did not sleep all night.
2. A traffic offense that would get a driver into trouble would be failing to stop at a stop sign.

B. Sample Answers

1. Dark clouds and thunder in the distance tell us that a storm is nigh.
2. The offense was unimportant, but we did not call each other for a long time.

C. 1. C; 2. B

Enrichment: Nature and Nurture, p. 170

Sample Answers

1. A. I admire athletes and people who are good at sports.
   B. I could do push-ups and sit-ups at home to get stronger. I could get a job after school to build up my endurance.
2. Shyness: He or she could make a point of asking people questions about themselves. The shy person could join a club or team to pursue a special interest.

   Laziness: He or she could make a schedule to do homework and chores around the house at certain times. Lazy people could plan to do the things they have to do before allowing themselves to watch television or to go out with friends.
3. People with quick tempers could count to ten to force themselves to calm down before speaking. They could try activities that teach a person to be calm and in control, such as yoga or karate. They could take a deep breath and walk away when they begin to feel angry.

Poetry Collections: Shel Silverstein, Octavio Paz, Rachel Field; William Shakespeare, Diana Chang, Gwendolyn Brooks

Build Language Skills: Vocabulary, p. 171

A. Sample Answers

1. ignores you
2. is precious, but not refined; has potential
3. became fearful
4. in trouble

B. 1. I hope to convey a message about the importance of recycling in my speech today.
2. Could you please explain why earthquakes happen?
3. For homework tonight, I have to paraphrase the first and last paragraphs of a story.
4. My favorite passage in *Tuck Everlasting* is the graveyard scene in the Epilogue when Tuck finds out what happened to Winnie.
5. The student council president will represent the school at the school board meeting.

Build Language Skills: Grammar, p. 172

A. 2. Arrow to: plays; predicate adjective
3. Arrow to: Sacramento; predicate noun
4. Arrow to: Kira and Naomi; predicate noun
5. Arrow to: sari; predicate noun
6. Arrow to: commercials; predicate adjective

B. Sample Answers

1. My favorite place is a <u>park</u> near where I live. 2. I always feel <u>happy</u> when I'm there. 3. The park is partly a <u>forest</u> with all kinds of plants and trees. 4. The forest is <u>shady</u> and <u>cool</u> in the summer. 5. The pine needles on the forest floor feel <u>soft</u> and <u>springy</u>.

1. PN; 2. PA; 3. PN; 4. PA; 5. PA

Unit 4 Resources: Poetry

© Pearson Education, Inc., publishing as Pearson Prentice Hall. All rights reserved.

223

Poetry Collection: William Shakespeare,
Diana Chang, Gwendolyn Brooks

Selection Test A, p. 173

Critical Reading

1. ANS: A DIF: Easy OBJ: Comprehension
2. ANS: D DIF: Easy OBJ: Comprehension
3. ANS: B DIF: Easy OBJ: Literary Analysis
4. ANS: B DIF: Easy OBJ: Reading
5. ANS: C DIF: Easy OBJ: Literary Analysis
6. ANS: A DIF: Easy OBJ: Interpretation
7. ANS: C DIF: Easy OBJ: Comprehension
8. ANS: B DIF: Easy OBJ: Reading
9. ANS: D DIF: Easy OBJ: Literary Analysis
10. ANS: D DIF: Easy OBJ: Interpretation
11. ANS: B DIF: Easy OBJ: Interpretation

Vocabulary and Grammar

12. ANS: C DIF: Easy OBJ: Vocabulary
13. ANS: D DIF: Easy OBJ: Vocabulary
14. ANS: D DIF: Easy OBJ: Vocabulary
15. ANS: A DIF: Easy OBJ: Grammar

Essay

16. Student essays should give two reasons for preferring
one of the poems and support the choice with logical
reasons that refer to the poems. For example, the choice
of "The Fairies' Lullaby" might be supported by the reasons that the details in the poem fully depict fairies in a
forest warning away animals and insects, and that the
chorus repetition of lullaby sounds is enjoyable.
Difficulty: *Easy*
Objective: *Essay*

17. Student essays should discuss how one sound device is
used in one poem. For example, repetition is used in
"Saying Yes," with the word *Really* emphasizing the
problem that the speaker has to deal with: people ques-
tioning who she is. The repetition of *Yes* shows that the
speaker has a positive attitude about herself; she knows
she is both Chinese and American, and she is proud of
her background.
Difficulty: *Easy*
Objective: *Essay*

Selection Test B, p. 176

Critical Reading

1. ANS: C DIF: Average OBJ: Comprehension
2. ANS: B DIF: Average OBJ: Interpretation
3. ANS: A DIF: Average OBJ: Literary Analysis
4. ANS: D DIF: Average OBJ: Reading

5. ANS: C DIF: Challenging OBJ: Comprehension
6. ANS: B DIF: Average OBJ: Literary Analysis
7. ANS: A DIF: Average OBJ: Interpretation
8. ANS: D DIF: Average OBJ: Interpretation
9. ANS: A DIF: Average OBJ: Reading
10. ANS: B DIF: Average OBJ: Reading
11. ANS: D DIF: Average OBJ: Interpretation
12. ANS: D DIF: Average OBJ: Literary Analysis
13. ANS: A DIF: Challenging OBJ: Comprehension
14. ANS: C DIF: Average OBJ: Interpretation

Vocabulary and Grammar

15. ANS: B DIF: Average OBJ: Vocabulary
16. ANS: D DIF: Average OBJ: Vocabulary
17. ANS: C DIF: Challenging OBJ: Vocabulary
18. ANS: A DIF: Average OBJ: Grammar

Essay

19. Student essays should compare the use of the three sound
devices in two of the poems. "The Fairies' Lullaby" uses alliteration ("spotted snakes," "lovely lady," "beetles black") and
repetition in having the chorus repeat a complete stanza, as
well as having the fairies repeat the word "not." Onomatopoeia is found in "Lulla, lulla, lullaby," which is repeated in
each stanza. "Cynthia in the Snow" uses alliteration
("laughs a lovely," "whitely whirs"), repetition (beginning
short sentences with "It" followed by a verb), and onomatopoeia ("SUSHES," "hushes," and "flitter-twitters").
Difficulty: *Average*
Objective: *Essay*

20. Student essays should define at least one difference and
one similarity. Examples of differences: The fairies' part
warns insects, snakes, and other scary creatures to stay
away and do no harm to the queen. Such threats usually
do not occur in lullabies. Also, the lullaby is sung to a
queen, not to a baby. Examples of similarities: In the second part, the chorus seems to be trying to lull the queen
to sleep. The second part is peaceful and soothing, with a
sound ("Lulla, lulla, lullaby") that is similar to lulling
sounds in other lullabies. The chorus part is repeated;
repetition often occurs in other lullabies. Suggestions for
modernizing might be to include more frightening things
like grizzly bears, toxic pollution, and earthquakes.
Difficulty: *Average*
Objective: *Essay*

Poetry by Alice Walker and Naomi Shihab Nye

Vocabulary Warm-up Exercises, p. 180

A. 1. rusted
2. circled

© Pearson Education, Inc., publishing as Pearson Prentice Hall. All rights reserved.

3. forgotten
4. naïve
5. infinite
6. neighborhood

B. Sample Answers

1. If someone gave me a piece of fruit and said it was <u>delicious</u>, I would try it because it should taste good.

2. I would feel satisfied after I had <u>completed</u> a difficult task because I would be happy to have finished it.

3. A <u>refreshing</u> drink of water will make a person feel stronger and less thirsty.

4. If a person is <u>savoring</u> the flavor of a new type of food, he or she will want to eat the food again because it is enjoyable to eat.

5. A cook could add <u>sweetness</u> to a dessert by adding sugar or honey.

6. When I take <u>delight</u> in something, I am happy I did it because it gave me great pleasure.

Reading Warm-up A, p. 181

Sample Answers

1. <u>his part of town</u>; I think my *neighborhood* is one of the most beautiful parts of Brooklyn.

2. <u>walking around the outside of it</u>; The firefighters *circled* the burning building before finding a safe place to enter.

3. (from being outside in the rain and wind); If metal is *rusted*, it has become a brownish color from being left out in wind and water.

4. <u>remembered</u>; I have *forgotten* to bring my umbrella out with me and now it is raining.

5. <u>Miguel used his own common sense and experience</u>; The *naïve* hiker was not experienced in climbing mountains.

6. (endless); When I look into the sky, I see an *infinite* number of stars.

Reading Warm-up B, p. 182

Sample Answers

1. <u>make you feel strong and fresh again</u>; I find that long, hot showers are *refreshing*.

2. <u>ate</u>; I enjoy *savoring* every bite of ice cream I eat.

3. (A fruit that tastes and smells pleasant is more likely to be eaten.); If something is *delicious*, that means it smells and tastes very good.

4. <u>finished</u>; The student *completed* her homework before she went to bed.

5. (natural sugars); *Sweetness* is the state of being sweet or full of a sweet flavor.

6. <u>pleasure</u>; Mary found *delight* in the beautiful, sunny weather.

Poetry by Alice Walker and Naomi Shihab Nye

Literary Analysis: Sensory Language, p. 183

A. Sample Answers

1. *the wavy green / Cherimoya*—sight, touch; *The black loudsmelling / & delicious / Durian*—sight, smell, taste, hearing; *The fleshy orange mango*—touch, sight, taste; *the spiky, whitehearted / Soursop*—touch, sight, taste

2. *the old people / of our neighborhood / are going up / into the air*—sight; *small white narcissus / sweetening winter*—sight, taste

Vocabulary Builder, p. 184

A. 1. C; 2. D; 3. A; 4. E; 5. B

B. Sample Answers

1. True. If a person is savoring a meal, he or she is enjoying it.

2. False. A sole winner is the only winner.

3. False. Phrasings are ways of speaking and cannot be strung into a necklace.

4. True. Melting icicles shine or sparkle in the sunlight.

5. True. Naïve people are unworldly and trusting.

Selection Test A, p. 186

Critical Reading

1. ANS: A	DIF: Easy	OBJ: Comprehension
2. ANS: C	DIF: Easy	OBJ: Interpretation
3. ANS: B	DIF: Easy	OBJ: Literary Analysis
4. ANS: C	DIF: Easy	OBJ: Comprehension
5. ANS: D	DIF: Easy	OBJ: Interpretation
6. ANS: A	DIF: Easy	OBJ: Interpretation
7. ANS: B	DIF: Easy	OBJ: Literary Analysis
8. ANS: D	DIF: Easy	OBJ: Interpretation
9. ANS: C	DIF: Easy	OBJ: Interpretation
10. ANS: A	DIF: Easy	OBJ: Comprehension
11. ANS: C	DIF: Easy	OBJ: Interpretation
12. ANS: B	DIF: Easy	OBJ: Literary Analysis

Vocabulary

13. ANS: A	DIF: Easy	OBJ: Vocabulary
14. ANS: D	DIF: Easy	OBJ: Vocabulary

Essay

15. Students should respond that "At First . . ." provides a list of the fruits in the speaker's garden and that "Alphabet" provides a list of objects in the speaker's neighborhood. They may say that Walker's list helps bring the

garden to life in the reader's mind and that it sends the message that the world is full of wonderful things. Students may say that Nye's list shows how empty the neighborhood is without the older people and that it sends the message that we should treasure familiar people and things. Accept other reasonable responses that are supported by details from the poems.

Difficulty: *Easy*

Objective: *Essay*

16. Students should respond that "At First . . ." appeals most strongly to the sense of taste and that "Alphabet" appeals most strongly to the sense of sight. They may say that Walker chose to focus on taste because she wants the reader to understand that life is sweet. They may say that Nye chose to focus on sight because she wants the reader to see the emptiness of the neighborhood as older people die. Accept all reasonable responses that are supported by poem details.

Difficulty: *Easy*

Objective: *Essay*

touch are well-suited to the subject of "At First . . ." because that poem is about experiencing the world as a garden—as a place full of many different tastes and textures.

Difficulty: *Average*

Objective: *Essay*

19. Students may reply that in "At First . . . ," Walker is trying to encourage young readers to experience life as fully as possible or to open their minds to new possibilities. They may cite the images of exotic fruits as the most powerful communicators of this message. Students may say that in "Alphabet," Nye is trying to encourage young readers to value their elderly friends and relatives or to appreciate how short and precious life is. They may cite the images of the empty yards or lawn chairs as the most powerful communicators of this message. Accept all reasonable responses that use details from the poems as support.

Difficulty: *Average*

Objective: *Essay*

Selection Test B, p. 189

Critical Reading

1. ANS: B	DIF: Average	OBJ: Comprehension
2. ANS: A	DIF: Average	OBJ: Literary Analysis
3. ANS: B	DIF: Challenging	OBJ: Interpretation
4. ANS: C	DIF: Average	OBJ: Interpretation
5. ANS: D	DIF: Average	OBJ: Comprehension
6. ANS: A	DIF: Average	OBJ: Interpretation
7. ANS: A	DIF: Average	OBJ: Literary Analysis
8. ANS: B	DIF: Challenging	OBJ: Interpretation
9. ANS: C	DIF: Average	OBJ: Comprehension
10. ANS: D	DIF: Average	OBJ: Literary Analysis
11. ANS: A	DIF: Challenging	OBJ: Interpretation
12. ANS: A	DIF: Average	OBJ: Literary Analysis
13. ANS: B	DIF: Average	OBJ: Interpretation
14. ANS: C	DIF: Average	OBJ: Interpretation

Vocabulary

15. ANS: C	DIF: Average	OBJ: Vocabulary
16. ANS: D	DIF: Average	OBJ: Vocabulary
17. ANS: B	DIF: Average	OBJ: Vocabulary

Essay

18. Students should identify "Alphabet" as the poem appealing more strongly to sight and "At First . . ." as the poem appealing more strongly to taste and touch. They should note that sight-related images are well-suited to the subject of "Alphabet" because in that poem, the speaker is noticing signs of her older neighbors' absence, such as empty yards and rusty chairs. Students should note that images related to taste and

Writing Workshop—Unit 4, Part 2

Comparison-and-Contrast Essay: Integrating Grammar Skills, p. 193

A.
1. sport, entertainment, predicate nouns
2. helmets, pads, direct objects
3. serious, lasting, predicate adjectives
4. offense, defense, indirect objects

B.
1. Some organizations hold football and cheerleading camps.
2. Players must be strong and fit.
3. The coach showed the quarterback and me a new play.
4. Throwing a great pass takes skill and practice.

Spelling Workshop—Unit 4

Affixes: Prefixes and Suffixes, p. 194

A. 1. plentiful; 2. misunderstand; 3. cleanness; 4. movement; 5. education; 6. reexamine; 7. betrayal; 8. dissatisfied

B. Sample Answers
1. An underline education will enable a student to learn to communicate. A student who is unable to communicate thoughts will often be underline dissatisfied and frustrated with others. If a student were to underline misunderstand, he or she would have failed to get the message that was communicated.
2. underline Furious at his friend's underline betrayal, Malcom felt the underline tension mount in his body. He knew that any underline movement he made must be controlled as he did not want to start a fight.

© Pearson Education, Inc., publishing as Pearson Prentice Hall. All rights reserved.

Unit 4, Part 2 Answers

Benchmark Test 8, p. 197

MULTIPLE CHOICE

1. ANS: D
2. ANS: A
3. ANS: A
4. ANS: C
5. ANS: B
6. ANS: C
7. ANS: C
8. ANS: D
9. ANS: A
10. ANS: B
11. ANS: C
12. ANS: C
13. ANS: D
14. ANS: B
15. ANS: D
16. ANS: C
17. ANS: D
18. ANS: A
19. ANS: C
20. ANS: B
21. ANS: B
22. ANS: D
23. ANS: C
24. ANS: C
25. ANS: B
26. ANS: B
27. ANS: B
28. ANS: C
29. ANS: A
30. ANS: D
31. ANS: C

ESSAY

32. Students' sentences should explain a humorous topic for a limerick. They should list two rhyming words that relate to their limerick topic.

33. Students' lists should contain well-reasoned similarities and differences.

© Pearson Education, Inc., publishing as Pearson Prentice Hall. All rights reserved.